Chapter 1
Addition and Subtraction of Whole Numbers

Exercise 1A (p. 2) — For discussion

Exercise 1B (p. 2)

1. 38	**4.** 436	**7.** 72
2. 18	**5.** 420	**8.** 970
3. 261	**6.** 402	**9.** fifty-six

10. one hundred and twelve
11. six hundred and seven
12. three hundred and ten
13. three hundred and four
14. two hundred and seventy-six
15. seventy-nine
16. one hundred and thirty-one
17. seventeen sixty-two, nineteen seventy-five
18. 400   **19.** 10   **20.** 8   **21.** 21
22. 5000
23. a 6365   **b** 1839   **c** 3307   **d** 860
24. Because the largest digit required is 9 and you do not need a bead for zero.

Exercise 1C (p. 4)

1. a five   **c** five hundred
b fifty   **d** five thousand

2.
hundreds	tens	units
	6	7
7	8	2

3. a 362   **b** 9043   **c** 70   **d** 507   **e** 4800
4. a three hundred and sixty-two
b nine thousand and forty-three
c seventy
d five hundred and seven
e four thousand and eight hundred
5. a eight hundred   **c** five hundred
b eight   **d** seventy
6. a 2041   **b** 4340   **c** 19 024   **d** 30 006   **e** 5070
7. a four thousand and twenty-four
b fourteen thousand and six hundred
8. forty-two thousand, twelve thousand and seven
9. forty-three thousand and two hundred at Wembley.

Exercise 1D (p. 6)

1. 43, 403, 431   **3.** 99, 101, 909   **5.** 654
2. 281, 812, 821   **4.** 56, 85, 519   **6.** 350

7. b 35, 37, 53, 57, 73, 75, 357, 375, 537, 573, 735, 753
8. 5 (for five hundred, the 8 is only eighty)

Exercise 1E (p. 7)

1. $1 + 9, 2 + 8, 3 + 7, 4 + 6, 5 + 5$
2. 11   **5.** 18   **8.** 12   **11.** 13
3. 13   **6.** 13   **9.** 12   **12.** 14
4. 11   **7.** 11   **10.** 12   **13.** 14

14. Addition square
15. 16
16. a 15   **b** 11   **c** 12
17. $4 + 5 = 9, 6 + 9 = 15$

---

18. a 17   **b** 19   **c** 19
19. 22   **20.**
23. a
2	7	
9	5	1
4	3	8

24. 14, 17, 20
25. 19, 23, 27
26. 13, 21, 34,
27. a 11   **b** $2 + 6, 3 + 5, 4 + 4$

Exercise 1F (p. 9)

1. 41	**10.** 80	**19.** 37	**28.** 886
2. 82	**11.** 431	**20.** 124	**29.** 643
3. 73	**12.** 840	**21.** 78 p	**30.** 193 cm
4. 86	**13.** 85	**22.** yes	**31.** 211
5. 69	**14.** 40	**23.** 469	**32.** 361
6. 91	**15.** 29	**24.** 993	**33.** 603
7. 181	**16.** 54	**25.** 820	**34.** 103
8. 257	**17.** 84	**26.** 925	**35.** 149
9. 558	**18.** 51	**27.** 491	**36.** 91

37. a yes   **b** yes   **c** no
38. a 743   **b** 159   **c** 107
39. $16 + 20 > 33$ and she won 27
40. a 14   **b** yes   **c** 24
41. a 22   **b** 19
42. 1 p, 2 p, 4 p, 8 p, 16 p, 32 p, 64 p, £1.28, £2.56, £5.12, Total £10.23. The amount to be saved each week gets bigger very rapidly !
43. a 18   **b** 45   **c** 55

Exercise 1G (p. 13)

1. 5	**8.** 8	**15.** 11
2. 3	**9.** 12	**16.** 8
3. 9	**10.** 15	**17.** 4
4. 7	**11.** 9	**18.** 5
5. 7	**12.** 8	**19.** 6
6. 6	**13.** 13	**20.** 14
7. 8	**14.** 3	**21.** 85, 80, 75, 70

22. 84, 79, 74, 69, 64, 59   **24.** 18
23. 52, 45, 38, 31, 24, 17   **25. a** no   **b** no   **c** yes

Exercise 1H (p. 14)

1. 21	**12.** 33	**23.** 73	**34.** 33 p
2. 21	**13.** 29	**24.** 126	**35.** 37 p
3. 25	**14.** 18	**25.** 470	**36.** 27
4. 13	**15.** 58	**26.** 354	**37.** 26
5. 19	**16.** 4	**27.** 287	**38.** 67
6. 27	**17.** 159	**28.** 178	**39.** £3.44
7. 6	**18.** 78	**29.** 187	**40.** 464
8. 15	**19.** 27	**30.** 8	**41.** eighty-nine
9. 14	**20.** 4	**31.** 255	**42.** 287
10. 69	**21.** 211	**32.** 279	**43.** 36
11. 92	**22.** 218	**33.** 73 cm	**44.** 6483

45. 240   **48.** 7500 m
46. 79, 72, 65, 58, 51   **49.** 318
47. 94, 82, 70, 58, 46   **50.** 168

51. a 6   **b** 9   **c** 9   **d** 4   **e** 8   **f** 7
52. £29

Exercise 1I (p. 17)

1. fifty

2. 89, 98, 808, 880

3. a 27   **b** 58   **c** 341   **d** 67

4. $6 - 5 + 4 + 3 - 2$ or $6 + 5 - 4 - 3 + 2$

5. 594

6. 156 cm

7. 834

8. 703

9. 39, 36, 33, 30, 27, 24, 21, 18, 15, 12

Exercise 1J (p. 18)

1. 410   **6.** 167

2. 437   **7.** 61

3. 1046   **8.** 29

4. 110   **9.** $152 + 39 = 191$

5. 282   **10.** 100

Puzzles (p. 18)

1. Put the 9 with 1, 2, 3

2.

4	2		8
	4	1	6
1	3	5	
9		7	3

3.

2	9	4
7	5	3
6	1	8

4. 159

5.

11	18	25	2	9
10	12	19	21	3
4	6	13	20	22
23	5	7	14	16
17	24	1	8	15

Chapter 2
Multiplication and Division of Whole Numbers

Exercise 2A (p. 21) — For discussion

Exercise 2B (p. 22)

1. 63   **2.** 32   **3.** 45

4.

×	0	1	2	3	4	5	6	7	8	9
0	0	0	0	0	0	0	0	0	0	0
1	0	1	2	3	4	5	6	7	8	9
2	0	2	4	6	8	10	12	14	16	18
3	0	3	6	9	12	15	18	21	24	27
4	0	4	8	12	16	20	24	28	32	36
5	0	5	10	15	20	25	30	35	40	45
6	0	6	12	18	24	30	36	42	48	54
7	0	7	14	21	28	35	42	49	56	63
8	0	8	16	24	32	40	48	56	64	72
9	0	9	18	27	36	45	54	63	72	81

5. a 28   **b** 21   **c** 18   **d** 18

6. a 24   **b** 20

7. a 36   **b** 30

8. 63, yes

9. 40

10. a 30   **b** 28   **c** 24   **d** 36   **e** 48

11. a 4   **b** 4   **c** 2

12. a 24, 24   **b** $4 + 4 + 4 + 4 + 4 + 4$

13. a $5 + 5 + 5, 3 + 3 + 3 + 3 + 3$

   b see **15**

   c i 9   **ii** 4,5

14. a 9   **b** 3   **c** 6   **d** 5   **e** 6   **f** 9

15. b (and **13. b**) Open to discussion — the totals are the same, but the groupings represented are not.

Exercise 2C (p. 25)

1. a 90   **b** 1428   **c** 288

2. a 51   **b** 92   **c** 136   **d** 238   **e** 125   **f** 378

3. 46   **11.** 144   **19.** 536   **27.** 1989

4. 126   **12.** 415   **20.** 657   **28.** 844

5. 104   **13.** 141   **21.** 168   **29.** 2859

6. 304   **14.** 324   **22.** 224   **30.** 1632

7. 290   **15.** 126   **23.** 608   **31.** 2628

8. 93   **16.** 588   **24.** 2456   **32.** 2184

9. 100   **17.** 292   **25.** 768   **33.** 852

10. 144   **18.** 162   **26.** 388   **34.** 2565

35. a 24   **b** 36   **c** 32   **d** 36   **e** 27   **f** 60

36. a 120   **b** 126   **c** 360   **d** 420   **e** 120   **f** 980

37. £1.12   **39.** £2.56   **41.** 3612 g

38. 344   **40.** 420 minutes

42. a 192, 768

   b 7, 14, 28, 56, 112

   c Start with 5 and multiply by 5

43. too little, estimate 130×6

44. a 7   **b** 3   **c** 2

45. 4 – you only need to multiply the units, $6 \times 7 \times 2 = 84$

46. £1250

Exercise 2D (p. 28)

1. 6   **5.** 8   **9.** 7

2. 4   **6.** 6   **10.** 9

3. 5   **7.** 9   **11.** 9

4. 8   **8.** 6   **12. a** 7,7   **b** 7,7

13. a right, $9 \times 3 = 27$ **c** wrong, $9 \times 7 = 63$

   b wrong, $8 \times 4 = 32$

14. a 4   **c** 4   **e** all the same

   b 4   **d** 4

15. 6, $12 \div 2 = 6$

16. $9 \times 7 = 63$

17. a 4   **c** $12 \div 3 = 4$

   b 4   **d** $12 \div 3 = 4$

Exercise 2E (p. 29)

1. >   **4.** <   **7.** <

2. <   **5.** =   **8.** >

3. <   **6.** >   **9.** >

10. 7, rem 3   **15.** 9. rem 1   **20.** 6, rem 3

11. 6, rem 8   **16.** 9, rem 1   **21.** 9, rem 6

12. 6, rem 2   **17.** 8, rem 7   **22.** 5, rem 1

13. 7, rem 5   **18.** 8, rem 2   **23.** 7, rem 2

14. 8, rem 2   **19.** 8, rem 3

24. a 9

   b 10

   c The remaining 3 half fill the tenth box.

25. a 5   **b** no   **c** five full rows would be 30.

26. a 6, rem 2

   b 6, rem 2

   c $32 \div 5 = 6$, rem 2 $32 \div 6 = 5$, rem 2

Exercise 2F (p. 32)

1. 18, rem 3   **9.** 48, rem 1   **17.** 8, rem 3
2. 16, rem 3   **10.** 14, rem 3   **18.** 13
3. 9, rem 5   **11.** 20, rem 3   **19.** 13, rem 1
4. 29   **12.** 23   **20.** 17, rem 3
5. 14   **13.** 13, rem 4   **21.** 7, rem 4
6. 27   **14.** 9, rem 6   **22.** 16
7. 19   **15.** 12, rem 1
8. 18   **16.** 13

Exercise 2G (p. 33)

1. 171   **10.** 1167   **19.** 183
2. 213   **11.** 440, rem 3   **20.** 353
3. 274   **12.** 2414, rem 1   **21.** 1727, rem 2
4. 32, rem 6   **13.** 351, rem 3   **22.** 13, 1 p
5. 231   **14.** 1067, rem 3   **23.** 15, 2
6. 103   **15.** 1479, rem 4   **24.** £41
7. 201, rem 2   **16.** 2193   **25.** 25
8. 81, rem 3   **17.** 1214   **26.** 16, 8, 4, 2, 1
9. 85   **18.** 198, rem 6   **27.** 625, 125, 25, 5, 1

28 a 26   **b** 26
29 a 28   **b** 28, rem 1   **c** 28
30 a 7   **b** 428 ÷ 2 = 214   **c** 549 ÷ 7 = 78, rem 3

Exercise 2H (p. 35)

1. 70   **18.** 12 600   **35.** 54 000
2. 80   **19.** 1240   **36.** 38 920
3. 270   **20.** 7800   **37.** 24 300
4. 256 000   **21.** 2600   **38.** 35 100
5. 600   **22.** 14 600   **39.** 42 800
6. 9000   **23.** 1740   **40.** 19 200
7. 8200   **24.** 6630   **41.** 8800
8. 240   **25.** 36 300   **42.** 19 000
9. 320   **26.** 146 000   **43.** 59 920
10. 47 000   **27.** 16 800   **44.** 8000
11. 360   **28.** 6720   **45.** 2000
12. 5600   **29.** 35 100   **46.** 7000 cm
13. 1600   **30.** 9420   **47.** £2800
14. 2200   **31.** 23 600   **48.** 19 200
15. 1080   **32.** 6160   **49.** A and C
16. 20 000   **33.** 70 000   **50.** B and C
17. 420   **34.** 48 720

51. That is only 5 balloons in each packet, you need another nought for the 50.

Exercise 2I (p. 37)

1. a 7   **b** 40   **c** 600   **d** 56   **e** 480
2. a 8   **b** 90   **c** 54   **d** 2   **e** 120
3. 30   **4.** 8   **5.** 24   **6.** A

7. 250 ÷ 10, 2500 ÷ 10, 25 × 100
8. 360 ÷ 10, 4200 ÷ 100, 42 × 10, 36 × 100
9. 780   **10.** 240   **11.** 12, rem 4

Exercise 2J (p. 38)

1. 108, 52, 56, 27   **7.** 5, rem 6
2. yes   **8. a** 24   **b** 90
3. a 60   **b** 300   **9.** 11
4. 13   **10.** 37
5. 7 × 8, by 2   **11.** 2240
6. £6.75

Puzzles (p. 39)

1.

1	6	1
3	■	2
2	7	6

2. 13
3. Reading clockwise round the circle 3, 15, 5, 50, 10, 60, 6, 18, in the centre 30.

Chapter 3
Collecting and Displaying Data

Exercise 3A (p. 41) — For discussion

Exercise 3B (p. 43)

1. a 27
   b Table should show these frequencies 0–5, 1–13, 2–4, 3–3, 4–2
2. S–14, V–7, C–7, P–8, Total 36
3. R–17, G–3, B–4, Y–14, P–6, Total 44
4. 22–1, 23–10, 24–15, 25–11, 26–4, 27–3, Total 44
5. 1–19, 2–13, 3–3, 4–5, Total 40

Exercise 3C (p. 44) — For discussion

Exercise 3D (p. 46)

1. a 55 vehicles
   b Car
   c

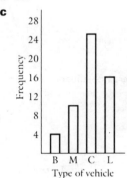

2. a 52 children
   b

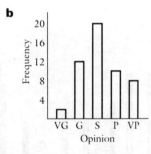

3. a Plain salted crisps
   b

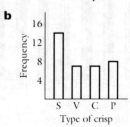

4. a Red

b

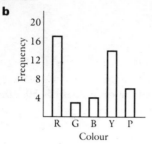

5. a 1

b

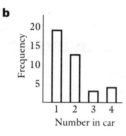

Exercise 3E (p. 47)

1. a 8   **b** 1,1   **c** 8   **d** 28   **e** 43

2. a 6   **b** Art   **c** French   **d** 38

3. a Brotton, 7000   **b** 10 000   **c** Castle Hill

Exercise 3F (p. 49)

1. a 7 car lengths

  b one car length for every 10 mph

  c Cars vary in length. It depends on the condition of tyres, brakes, road surface etc.

2. a Off peak electric

  b Gas

  c Solid fuel

  d Gas

3. a Margate

  b June

  c Aberdeen–December, Margate–January

4. a £2500

  b about $\frac{3}{4}$

  c It starts at 2000.

  d Start at 0.

5. a 13

  b Labour

  c 1945 and 1987

  d

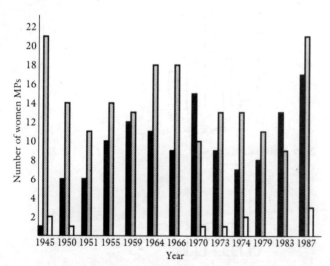

e i The first graph.   **ii** The second graph

Exercise 3G (p. 51)

1. a 1st –10, 2nd – 13, 3rd – 10, 4th – 22

  b Road deaths are increasing.

2. a French

  b French – 18, Maths – 15, History – 11, Geography – 12, English – 16, Total – 72

  c Not very, it's fun but fiddly to draw and interpret.

3. a It's increasing.

  b The width has been changed as well as the height, making the changes in area much greater.

Chapter 4
Negative Numbers

Exercise 4A (p. 54) — For discussion

Exercise 4B (p. 55)

1. 4 degrees below zero   **4.** 1 degree below zero

2. 8 degrees above zero   **5.** 26 degrees above zero

3. 11 degrees below zero   **6.** 14 degrees above zero

7. a 1 °C   **b** 6 °C   **c** 19 °C   **d** −2 °C   **e** −8 °C

8. −9 °C   **11.** 11 °C   **14.** −3 °C

9. higher   **12.** 2 °C   **15.** 1 °C

10. higher   **13.** 6 °C   **16.** 0 °C

17.

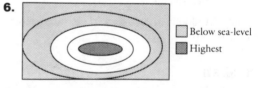

18. −6 °C, −1 °C

19. −6 °C

20. −6 °C, −1 °C, 0 °C, 4 °C, 8 °C

21. a <   **b** >   **c** <   **d** <   **e** >   **f** <

22. 6 degrees below zero

Exercise 4C (p. 57)

1. 60 m above sea-level   **3.** 100 m below sea-level

2. 8000 m above sea-level   **4.** at sea-level

5. 700 m below sea-level

6.

(diagram: concentric ellipses)

□ Below sea-level
■ Highest

7. a 8   **b** −2   **c** 10   **d** −1

8. Basement   **11.** −1   **14.** 2

9. −2   **12.** −2   **15.** −1

10. 2   **13.** 8   **16.** −3

Exercise 4D (p. 59)

1. a −10 seconds   **b** +5 seconds

2. a lift-off minus one second   **b** lift-off plus 8 seconds

3. a −10 seconds   **b** +40 seconds

4. a −3 seconds   **b** +2 seconds

5. The launch of 'Orion' was aborted 2 minutes before it was due to lift off.

6. The second-stage rockets are designed to fire 2 minutes after lift-off.

Exercise 4E (p. 60)

1. a −5 °C   **b** 11 °C   **c** 29 °C   **d** −9 °C
2. 8 °C
3. 2 °C
4. 10 °C
5. −6 °C
6. 11 °C
7. a risen   **b** 6 °C
8. a fallen   **b** 16 °C
9. −3 + 5 = 2
10. −5 + 4 = −1
11. −2 + 4 = 2
12. −7 + 8 = 1

13. The temperature starts at 3 degrees below zero and rises 7 degrees to +4 degrees.

14. The temperature starts at −9 °C and rises 4 degrees to −5 °C.

15. The temperature starts at −6 °C and rises 3 degrees to −3 °C.

16. 3 °C
17. 5 °C
18. −2 °C
19. −1 °C
20. 2 °C
21. 7 °C

Exercise 4F (p. 62)

1. 3 °C
2. −11 °C
3. −3 °C
4. −11 °C
5. 15 °C
6. a fallen   **b** 10 °C
7. 4 − 9 = −5
8. −1 − 10 = −11
9. −3 − 6 = −9

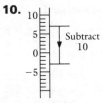
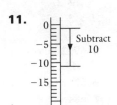

14. −2 °C
15. −6 °C
16. −10 °C
17. −8 °C
18. −8 °C
19. −8 °C
20. −16 °C
21. 7 °C
22. 12 °C
23. 5 °C
24. −5 °C
25. −11 °C
26. 8 °C
27. −9 °C
28. −9 °C
29. 25 °C
30. −5 °C
31. −16 °C
32. a −930   **b** 1295 − 365 =
33. She keyed in 36 − 55 =

Exercise 4G (p. 64)

1. a 6 °C   **b** 5 °C   **c** −5 °C
2. 4
3. −3 + 12 = 9
4. −2
5. 12 − 12 = 0
6. zero
7. 7 − 9 = −2

---

8. −1 + 4 = 3, Angela starts in the garage, rises 4 floors and arrives on the 3rd floor.
9. 12   **10.** 10
11. a Basement   **b** 8 − 10 + 6 = 4
12. a The temperature starts at −16 °C and rises 9 degrees.
   b The temperature starts at 24 °C and falls 30 degrees.
   c The temperature starts at −5 °C and falls 9 degrees.
   d The temperature starts at −12 °C and rises 18 degrees.
13. a −7 °C   **b** −6 °C   **c** −14 °C   **d** 6 °C

Chapter 5
Symmetry

Exercise 5A (p. 68) — For discussion

Exercise 5B (p. 68)

1. yes
2. yes
3. yes
4. no
5. no
6. yes
7. yes
8. no
9. yes
10. 1
11. 3
12. 1
13. 1
14. 1
15. 1
16. 4
17. 3
18. 1
19. no
20. 2
21. no

Exercise 5C (p. 70)

1. A2, B4, C5, D6, E1, F3

2.

3.

4.

5.
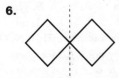

6.

7.
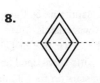

8.
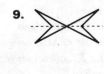

9.
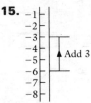

10. EVE DID HER HOMEWORK
11. a no   **b** & **c** 12:00, 06:00
12. e.g. swap a cup with the corresponding jug.
13. a A, B, D, F, G   **b** C, E, H

Exercise 5D (p. 73)

1.

6.

2.

7.

3.

8.

4.

9.

5.

10.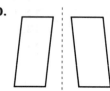

Exercise 5E (p. 75)

1. yes	**4.** yes	**7.** no
2. yes	**5.** yes	**8.** yes
3. no	**6.** no	**9.** yes

10. any four from: H, I, N, O, S, X, Z

11. Any not listed for question 10

12. b & c

13. a & c

14. a & c

15. a C **b** A, E **c** D **d** A & E

16. a A, C **b** B **c** D, E **d** A, D, E

17. a B

  b change it to look like A or D

  c D

18. a i Mauritania & European Council **iii** none

  ii Switzerland **iv** Switzerland

  (The Cedar tree of Lebanon and the stars for
  St Kitts-Nevis spoil any symmetry. Look carefully at
  the stars on the EC flag).

  b i Mauritania & European Council

  ii none

  iii & iv Switzerland

  (The Isle of Man *design* has rotational symmetry or
  order 3, but the whole flag does not have rotational
  symmetry).

Exercise 5F (p. 80)

Squares: **13a**

Rectangles: **12a**, **13c**, **14b**

Triangles: **5**, **7**, **12d**

Exercise 5G (p. 80)

1.   **2.**  **3.**

4. B, C

5. a A, D **b** B, C, E **c** A, D **d** F

6. a

  b

  c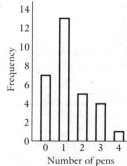

SUMMARY 1

Revision Exercise 1.1 (p. 85)

1. a 27 **b** 672 **c** 4306

2. a forty-five

  b seven hundred and thirty-seven

  c three thousand eight hundred and ninety-three

3. a seven **c** seventy

  b seven hundred **d** seven thousand

4. 427, 429, 470, 472, 474

5. a $124 + 356 = 480$ **d** $573 - 314 = 259$

  b $437 + 148 = 585$ **e** $315 \div 7 = 45$

  c $429 - 137 = 292$ **f** $564 \div 2 = 282$

6. Two extra. $8 \times 9 = 72$

7. a i 24 **ii** 60 **iii** 36 **iv** 27

  b i Wrong, $6 \times 9 = 54$ **iii** Wrong, $9 \times 3 = 27$

  ii Right, $4 \times 12 = 48$

8. a 180 miles **b** 2340 miles **c** 6912 miles

9. a $=$ **b** $>$ **c** $<$ **d** $<$

10. a 28 **c** 161 **e** 52, rem 5

  b 21, rem 3 **d** 145 **f** 684

Revision Exercise 1.2 (p. 86)

1. 30

2. Frequencies: 0–7, 1–13, 2–5, 3–4, 4–1, Total 30

3.

(bar chart: Frequency (y-axis 0 to 14) vs Number of pens in pencil case (x-axis 0 to 4))

4. a 3 °C **b** −4 °C **c** 16 °C
5. a < **b** < **c** < **d** <
6. a 1 °C **b** −3 °C **c** −7 °C **d** 1 °C
7. a D **b** A, E **c** B, F **d** C
8. B, C, D, F

9. A **B** **C** **D**

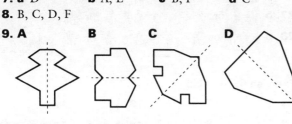

10. a C, F **b** B, D, E **c** A

Revision Exercise 1.3 (p. 88)

1. a i 106 **ii** 106 same **b i** 7 **ii** −7 different
2. 44
3. a 12 **b** 9 **c** 8 **d** 8
4. a 21, rem 2 **b** 123 **c** 421 **d** 879
5. £2.22, £2.78
6. a i Tuesday **ii** Thursday
  b i 5 **ii** 4
  c 19
  d 57
7. a 12 °C **b** 0 °C **c** −3 °C
8. a −3 °C **b** 5 °C **c** −2 °C **d** −7 °C
9. a **b** **c** **d**

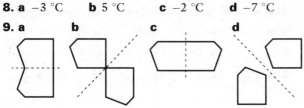

10. B, C, F have rotational symmetry, A, D, E do not.

Revision Exercise 1.4 (p. 90)

1. a i 30 **ii** 58 **iii** 4 **iv** 22
  b i 26 **ii** 37 **iii** 203 **iv** 317
2. 330
3. a 292 **b** 410 **c** 282 **d** 460 **e** 168 **f** 306
4. £68 750
5. a 243 × 3 = 729
  b 449 × 6 = 2694
  c 503 × 9 = 4527
6.

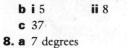

7. a i Football **ii** Tennis
  b i 5 **ii** 8
  c 37
8. a 7 degrees **b** 15 degrees
9. a **b** **c**

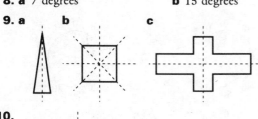

10.

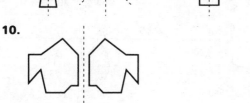

Chapter 6
Fractions

Exercise 6A (p. 93)

1. $\frac{3}{8}$ **7.** $\frac{1}{6}$ **13.** $\frac{1}{2}$ **19.** $\frac{1}{4}$
2. $\frac{5}{6}$ **8.** $\frac{1}{4}$ **14.** $\frac{3}{4}$ **20.** $\frac{1}{2}$
3. $\frac{3}{5}$ **9.** $\frac{1}{3}$ **15.** $\frac{1}{2}$ **21.** $\frac{1}{3}$
4. $\frac{3}{4}$ **10.** $\frac{3}{5}$ **16.** $\frac{3}{4}$ **22.** 1
5. $\frac{1}{3}$ **11.** $\frac{3}{4}$ **17.** $\frac{1}{3}$ **23.** $\frac{1}{2}$
6. $\frac{1}{6}$ **12.** $\frac{5}{9}$ **18.** $\frac{1}{4}$ **24.** 0

Exercise 6B (p. 95)

1. 1 shaded **7.** 1 shaded **13.** 12 shaded
2. 5 shaded **8.** 1 shaded **14.** 2 shaded
3. 7 shaded **9.** 3 shaded **15.** 10 shaded
4. 3 shaded **10.** 5 shaded **16.** 4 shaded
5. 5 shaded **11.** 15 shaded
6. 3 shaded **12.** 6 shaded

Exercise 6C (p. 97)

1. 2, 5 **4.** 13, 20 **7.** 4, 9 **10.** 21, 100
2. 3, 7 **5.** 3, 8 **8.** 5, 16 **11.** 9, 13
3. 9, 11 **6.** 1, 12 **9.** 11, 15 **12.** 31, 36

13. a $\frac{1}{3}$ **b** $\frac{3}{4}$ **c** $\frac{4}{5}$ **d** $\frac{7}{12}$ **e** $\frac{13}{20}$ **f** $\frac{5}{8}$
14. a half **c** seven-tenths **e** eleven-fifteenths
  b three-fifths **d** five-twelfths **f** three-eighths
15. a $\frac{3}{7}$ **b** $\frac{7}{12}$ **c** $\frac{11}{20}$ **d** $\frac{13}{15}$

Exercise 6D (p. 99)

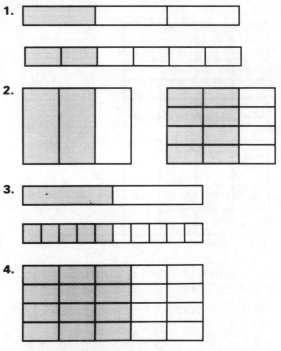

5.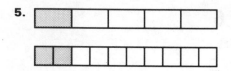

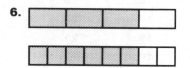

6.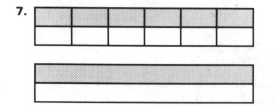

7.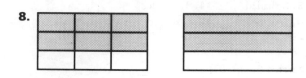

8.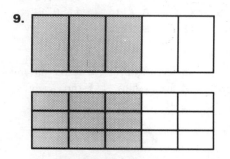

9.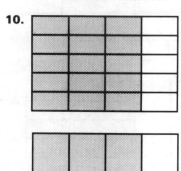

10.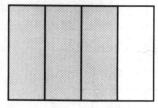

11. $\frac{2}{6}$　　**14.** $\frac{9}{12}$　　**17.** $\frac{6}{16}$

12. $\frac{4}{6}$　　**15.** $\frac{8}{20}$　　**18.** $\frac{20}{20}$

13. $\frac{5}{10}$　　**16.** $\frac{20}{48}$　　**19.** $\frac{10}{35}$

20. a $\frac{6}{12}$　**b** $\frac{8}{12}$　**c** $\frac{9}{12}$　**d** $\frac{2}{12}$　**e** $\frac{10}{12}$

21. a $\frac{10}{20}$　**b** $\frac{16}{20}$　**c** $\frac{14}{20}$　**d** $\frac{15}{20}$　**e** $\frac{18}{20}$

22. a $\frac{6}{24}$　**b** $\frac{20}{24}$　**c** $\frac{14}{24}$　**d** $\frac{8}{24}$　**e** $\frac{15}{24}$

23. a $\frac{6}{100}$　**c** $\frac{60}{100}$　**e** $\frac{16}{100}$　**g** $\frac{75}{100}$

b $\frac{35}{100}$　**d** $\frac{25}{100}$　**f** $\frac{50}{100}$

24. a $\frac{12}{14}$　**b** $\frac{12}{16}$　**c** $\frac{12}{27}$　**d** $\frac{12}{48}$　**e** $\frac{12}{18}$

25. a yes　**b** no　**c** no　**d** yes　**e** yes

26. a $\frac{20}{42}$　**b** $\frac{20}{24}$　**c** $\frac{20}{45}$　**d** $\frac{20}{30}$　**e** $\frac{20}{100}$

27. b $\frac{2}{3} = \frac{4}{6}$ or $\frac{6}{9}$　　**c** $\frac{3}{10} = \frac{30}{100}$ or $\frac{33}{110}$

28. c $\frac{3}{8} = \frac{12}{32}$ or $\frac{9}{24}$　　**e** $\frac{5}{11} = \frac{55}{121}$ or $\frac{50}{110}$

Exercise 6E (p. 102)

1. $\frac{1}{2}$　　**7.** $\frac{2}{5}$　　**13.** $\frac{1}{3}$　　**19.** $\frac{1}{3}, \frac{2}{3}$

2. $\frac{1}{6}$　　**8.** $\frac{5}{6}$　　**14.** $\frac{4}{5}$　　**20.** $\frac{4}{9}, \frac{5}{9}$

3. $\frac{1}{3}$　　**9.** $\frac{2}{3}$　　**15.** $\frac{1}{6}$　　**21.** $\frac{5}{8}, \frac{3}{8}$

4. $\frac{1}{4}$　　**10.** $\frac{3}{4}$　　**16.** $\frac{2}{7}$　　**22.** $\frac{3}{5}, \frac{2}{5}$

5. $\frac{3}{4}$　　**11.** $\frac{1}{2}$　　**17.** $\frac{3}{5}, \frac{2}{5}$　　**23.** $\frac{1}{3}, \frac{2}{3}$

6. $\frac{3}{4}$　　**12.** $\frac{5}{6}$　　**18.** $\frac{9}{20}, \frac{11}{20}$　　**24.** $\frac{3}{5}, \frac{2}{5}$

25. b $\frac{5}{6}$　　**d** $\frac{1}{6}$

26. a $\frac{1}{3}$　**b** $\frac{1}{3}$　**c** $\frac{1}{2}$　**d** $\frac{2}{3}$

Exercise 6F (p. 106)

1. $\frac{1}{3}, \frac{2}{3}$　　**2.** $\frac{4}{9}, \frac{5}{9}$　　**3.** $\frac{1}{3}, \frac{2}{3}$　　**4.** $\frac{2}{3}, \frac{1}{3}$

5. a i 9　**ii** 20　　**b i** eleven-twelfths　**ii** $\frac{10}{17}$

6. a $\frac{42}{100}$　**b** $\frac{76}{100}$　**c** $\frac{45}{100}$　**d** $\frac{80}{100}$　**e** $\frac{75}{100}$

7. a $\frac{24}{26}$　**b** $\frac{24}{28}$　**c** $\frac{24}{54}$　**d** $\frac{24}{80}$　**e** $\frac{24}{60}$

8. a $\frac{1}{3}$　**b** $\frac{1}{3}$　**c** $\frac{4}{5}$　**d** $\frac{9}{10}$　**e** $\frac{3}{20}$

Chapter 7
Percentages

Exercise 7A (p. 110)

1. 20%　**7.** 90%　**13.** 83%　**19.** 54%　**25.** 20%

2. 35%　**8.** 28%　**14.** 99%　**20.** 28%　**26.** 85%

3. 66%　**9.** 100%　**15.** 100%　**21.** 8%　**27.** 50%

4. 50%　**10.** 37%　**16.** 14%　**22.** 40%　**28.** 60%

5. 72%　**11.** 45%　**17.** 69%　**23.** 45%　**29.** 70%

6. 81%　**12.** 10%　**18.** 1%　**24.** 25%　**30.** 75%

31.

32.

33.

34.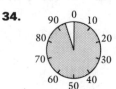

35.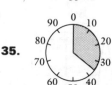

36.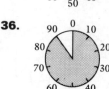

Exercise 7B (p. 112)

1.

8.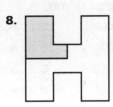

2.

9.

3.

10.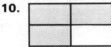

4.

11.

5.

12.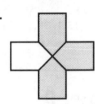

6.

13.

7.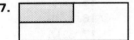

Exercise 7C (p. 114)

1. $\frac{3}{5}$ **6.** $\frac{19}{20}$ **11.** 28%   **16.** $\frac{1}{2}$

2. $\frac{4}{5}$ **7.** $\frac{12}{25}$ **12.** $\frac{1}{4}$ **17.** 41%

3. $\frac{7}{20}$ **8.** $\frac{2}{25}$ **13.** $\frac{1}{5}$ **18.** $\frac{1}{4}$

4. $\frac{1}{20}$ **9.** $\frac{17}{25}$ **14.** 80%

5. $\frac{3}{20}$ **10.** $\frac{8}{25}$ **15.** $\frac{3}{16}$

19. a 14%   **b** $\frac{7}{50}$

20. a 34%   **b** $\frac{17}{50}$

21. a 4%   **b** $\frac{24}{25}$

22. a i 34%   **ii** $\frac{17}{50}$ **b** 66%   **c** $\frac{33}{50}$

23. a 18%   **b** 82%   **c** $\frac{9}{50}$ **d** $\frac{41}{50}$

24. a $\frac{13}{20}$ **b** 65%

25. a 33%   **b** $\frac{23}{100}$ **c** $\frac{3}{4}$

26. a 25%   **b** 30%   **c** $\frac{9}{20}$

Exercise 7D (p. 116)

1. a 84%   **b** $\frac{21}{25}$

2. a 55%   **b** 35%

3. a   **b**

4. a $\frac{1}{6}$ **b** $\frac{3}{4}$

5. a $\frac{19}{20}$ **b** 5%

6. a i 24%   **ii** 76%   **b i** no   **ii** yes

Chapter 8
Decimals

Exercise 8A (p. 120)

1. 1 inch and 1 tenth of an inch
2. 1 inch and 7 tenths of an inch
3. 2 inches and 6 tenths of an inch
4. 1 inch and 2 tenths of an inch
5. 2 inches
6. 9 tenths of an inch
7. 2 inches and 7 tenths of an inch

Exercise 8B (p. 121)

1. 1.1 inches, 1.7 inches, 2.6 inches, 1.2 inches, 2.0 inches, 0.9 inches, 2.7 inches

2. 1.8 cm   **5.** 7.3 cm   **8.** 2.4 kg
3. 3.7 cm   **6.** 5.4 cm   **9.** 0.9 kg
4. 1.0 cm   **7.** 4.9 kg   **10.** 8.7 kg

Exercise 8C (p. 123)

1.

	tens	units	tenths
a	1	2 .	6
b		0 .	5
c		6 .	3
d		0 .	2
e		3 .	6
f	2	4 .	7
g		7 .	2
h	1	7 .	9

2. a two   **c** 2 tenths   **e** 2 tenths
    b twenty   **d** two

3. a seven   **c** seventy   **e** seven
    b 7 tenths   **d** 7 tenths

4. a fifty   **c** five, 5 tenths   **e** fifty, 5 tenths
    b five   **d** fifty, 5 tenths

5. 20.6, 21.5, 23.4
6. a 8.6, 12.9, 15.1   **c** 4.8, 7, 20
    b 15.5, 18, 20.1   **d** 1.2, 1.9, 2
7. 3.0 and 3
8. 5.0 and 5
9. 200, 20, 2, 2 tenths

Exercise 8D (p. 124)

1. 1.3 inches   **7.** 5.8 cm   **13.** 2.5 kg
2. 0.6 inches   **8.** 8.0 cm   **14.** 4.2 kg
3. 2.1 inches   **9.** 1.5 cm   **15.** 10.6 kg
4. 1.2 inches   **10.** 0.9 cm   **16.** 2.6 kg
5. 1.3 cm   **11.** 2.5 cm   **17.** 92.8 kg
6. 12.5 cm   **12.** 3.7 cm   **18.** 2.3 kg

Exercise 8E (p. 127)

	cm	0.1 cm	0.01 cm
1.	1	2	8
2.	10	4	4
3.	0	2	8
4.	15	7	1
5.	2	9	7
6.	20	4	4

	kg	0.1 kg	0.01 kg
7.	13	4	7
8.	7	9	3
8.	4	6	2
10.	5	3	6

Exercise 8F (p. 128)

1. 1.28 cm, 10.44 cm, 0.28 cm, 15.71 cm, 2.97 cm, 20.44 cm, 13.47 kg, 7.93 kg, 4.62 kg, 5.36 kg

2. 2.78 cm   4. 8.11 cm   6. 0.86 cm   8. 3.70 cm

3. 12.55 cm   5. 0.39 cm   7. 6.03 cm   9. 1.92 cm

Exercise 8G (p. 129)

1.	tens	units	.	tenths	hundredths
a	1	4	.	5	6
b		5	.	8	7
c		6	.	0	4
d	2	0	.	1	2
e		4	.	0	8
f	4	1	.	9	9
g	3	0	.	0	8
h	6	0	.	3	2

2. **a** seventy   **c** seven   **e** 7 hundredths
   b 7 tenths   **d** 7 hundredths

3. **a** four   **c** 4 hundredths   **e** 4 hundredths
   b 4 tenths   **d** forty

4. **a** three   **c** 3 hundredths   **e** three, 3 tenths
   b 3 hundredths   **d** thirty

5. 0.53

6. 1.71

7. 2.05, 2.5, 2.55

8. 24.1, 21.4, 12.04

9. **a** 3.4, 4.03, 4.3   **c** 1.57, 7.15, 15.7
   b 1.07, 1.7, 7.1   **d** 36.29, 36.92, 63.29

10. **a** 2.10, 2.1   **b** 1.40, 1.4   **c** 57, 57.0

11. **a** 512.66, 57.32, 25.89, 10.56, 3.45
   b 5 tenths, 5 hundreds, 5 hundredths, 5 units, 5 tens

Exercise 8H (p. 131)

1. 1.15 cm   4. 3.78 cm   7. 0.58   10. 2.96

2. 1.56 cm   5. 2.14 cm   8. 1.01   11. 5.48

3. 0.84 cm   6. 2.00 cm   9. 0.34   12. 3.82

Exercise 8I (p. 132)

1. $\frac{1}{5}$ 4. $\frac{1}{10}$ 7. $\frac{9}{10}$ 10. $\frac{1}{5}$

2. $\frac{7}{10}$ 5. $\frac{1}{2}$ 8. $\frac{7}{10}$ 11. $\frac{4}{5}$

3. $\frac{1}{2}$ 6. $\frac{3}{10}$ 9. $\frac{3}{5}$

Exercise 8J (p. 133)

1. **a** 0.67   **b** 67 hundredths   **c** $\frac{67}{100}$

2. **a** 0.94   **b** 94 hundredths   **c** $\frac{47}{50}$

3. **a** 0.51   **b** 51 hundredths   **c** $\frac{51}{100}$

4. **a** 0.32   **b** 32 hundredths   **c** $\frac{8}{25}$

5. **a** 5.57   **b** 557 hundredths   **c** $5\frac{57}{100}$

6. **a** 0.15   **b** 15 hundredths   **c** $\frac{3}{20}$

7 **a** 0.86   **b** 86 hundredths   **c** $\frac{43}{50}$

8. **a** 0.17   **b** 17 hundredths   **c** $\frac{17}{100}$

9. $\frac{4}{25}$ 13. $\frac{11}{25}$ 17. $\frac{2}{25}$ 21. $\frac{3}{5}$

10. $\frac{9}{25}$ 14. $\frac{11}{20}$ 18. $\frac{1}{100}$ 22. $\frac{3}{100}$

11. $\frac{3}{4}$ 15. $\frac{3}{10}$ 19. $\frac{4}{5}$ 23. $\frac{3}{20}$

12. $\frac{6}{25}$ 16. $\frac{23}{25}$ 20. $\frac{7}{20}$ 24. $\frac{81}{100}$

Exercise 8K (p. 134)

1. **a** 36 and 8 tenths °C   **b** 36.8 °C

2. **a** 3 tens 4 units 9 tenths   **b i** 9 tenths   **ii** fifty

3. 1.9 cm

4. 1.05 cm

5. **a** 3 kilograms, one tenth and 7 hundredths of a kilogram
   b 5 kilograms, 8 tenths and 3 hundredths of a kilogram

6. **a** seven   **b** 7 hundredths   **c** 7 tenths

7. 13.04, 13.4, 30.14, 31.4

8. **a** $\frac{3}{5}$ **b** $\frac{9}{20}$ **c** $\frac{31}{50}$ **d** $\frac{1}{20}$

Chapter 9
Adding and Subtracting Decimals

Exercise 9A (p. 138)

1. 3 cm   7. 102.6   13. 17.6

2. 4.2 cm   8. 4.4   14. 33.2

3. 3.8   9. 9.3   15. 58.6

4. 10.8   10. 30.2   16. 174.3

5. 13.5   11. 135.3   17. 321.1

6. 39.9   12. 232.2

18. **a** 23.4 cm   **b** 22.5 cm   **c** 45.9 cm

19. **a** 3.5 m   **b** 1.8 m

20. 8.5 m   23. 7.1 m   26. 6.3 m

21. 59.2 cm   24. 8.4 m   27. 3.0 m

22. 3.4 m   25. 5.7 m

Exercise 9B (p. 141)

1. 16.51 cm   9. 27.85   17. 11.59

2. 2.25 kg   10. 22.56   18. 84.11

3. 2.26 m   11. 30.29   19. 11.84

4. 7.26   12. 52.36   20. 11.09

5. 7.79   13. 0.25   21. 51.92

6. 10.25   14. 18.2   22. 21.44

7. 23.14   15. 51   23. 129.81

8. 18.74   16. 8.87   24. 1.81 cm

25. 5.37 m

26. **a** 9.88 cm   **b** 9.63 cm

27. 5.13 m   28. 5.66 m   29. 16.92 cm

Exercise 9C (p. 144)

1. 4.3 cm	**12.** 1.61	**23.** 13.23
2. 4.6 cm	**13.** 17.46	**24.** 28.39
3. 4.6 cm	**14.** 11.83	**25.** 0.13
4. 1.6	**15.** 15.76	**26.** 2.44
5. 1.3	**16.** 11.31	**27.** 48.51
6. 1.8	**17.** 6.85	**28.** 12.45 m
7. 3.2	**18.** 4.96	**29.** 0.27 m
8. 7.4	**19.** 5.82	**30.** 3.27 m
9. 3.9	**20.** 1.68	**31.** 0.84 kg
10. 4.3	**21.** 3.19	**32.** £5.88
11. 4.5	**22.** 1.45	**33.** 76 p, 0.63 tonnes

34. a $52 + 1.2 = 53.2$
  b $31.8 - 7.5 = 24.3$
  c $14.2 + 3.46 = 17.66$
35. a 6.92 °C
  b i 1.21 °C **ii** 2.99 °C
36. a 3.1 cm, 4.8 cm
  b $3.14 + 4.84 = 7.98$ (which rounds up to **8.0**) but $3.1 + 4.8 = 7.9$.
37. 4.3 cm

Exercise 9D (p. 147)

1. a 8.6	**b** 13.2
2. a 9.5	**b** 4.6
3. a 11.69	**b** 14.11
4. a 5.93	**b** 2.75
5. 2.99 km	
6. a 0.13 sec	**b** 10.00 sec

Puzzles (p. 147)

1. a i $1 + 0.31 + 0.21 + 0.42 = 1.94$
   ii $1 + 0.16 + 0.42 + 0.15 = 1.73$
  b i $1 + 0.31 + 0.16 + 0.42 + 0.43 + 0.21 = 2.53$
   ii $1 + 0.16 + 0.31 + 0.19 + 0.21 + 0.23 = 2.1$

2.

0.36	0.08	0.4
0.32	0.28	0.24
0.16	0.48	0.2

Chapter 10
Estimating and Using a Calculator

Exercise 10A (p. 149) — For discussion

Exercise 10B (p. 150)

1. a 40 mm **b** It's less than 45 mm
2. 700
3. a 800 kg **b** the one in the tens position
4. £400
5. 9000
6. 600

7. 80	**b** 90	**c** 50	**d** 70
8. a 400	**b** 200	**c** 700	**d** 200
9. a 80	**b** 30	**c** 100	
10. a 700	**b** 500	**c** 200	

11. 80 p
12. 400, 200

Exercise 10C (p. 153)

1. 80	**9.** 70	**17.** 1600	**25.** 9000
2. 150	**10.** 0	**18.** 3800	**26.** 7000
3. 50	**11.** 800	**19.** 1000	**27.** 35000
4. 630	**12.** 300	**20.** 2000	**28.** 94000
5. 10	**13.** 800	**21.** 7000	**29.** 17000
6. 40	**14.** 1200	**22.** 4000	**30.** 45000
7. 230	**15.** 1400	**23.** 5000	
8. 160	**16.** 500	**24.** 4000	

31. 2000 (arguably 1970) **33.** 380
32. 4000 **34 & 35** — for discussion

Exercise 10D (p. 155)

1. 3 g	**10.** 18 cm	**19.** 5 kg	**28.** 4 tonnes
2. 6 g	**11.** 87 cm	**20.** 27 kg	**29.** 53 mm
3. 11 g	**12.** 234 cm	**21.** 48 kg	**30.** 4 litres
4. 246 g	**13.** 5 m	**22.** 1 kg	**31.** 59 kg
5. 386 g	**14.** 9 m	**23.** 505 kg	**32.** 5 volts
6. 82 g	**15.** 57 m	**24.** 39 kg	**33.** 13 stones
7. 8 cm	**16.** 1 m	**25.** 4 kg	**34.** 2 amps
8. 6 cm	**17.** 427 m	**26.** 70 g	**35.** 13 oz
9. 26 cm	**18.** 1 m	**27.** 153 cm	**36.** 3 ohms

Exercise 10E (p. 157)

1. 70, 72	**12.** 600, 592
2. 600, 590	**14.** 12, 12.19
3. 40, 44	**16.** No, nearer 60 cm
4. 1400, 1421	**17. a** £1.30 **b** £1.25
5. 90, 81	**18.** No, nearer £300
6. 500, 568	**19.** 3200, correct ans 3024
7. 12, 11.69	**22.** 200 (or 300), correct ans 282,
8. 1, 1.43	2000 ÷ 7 is less than 300
9. 100 or 180, 180.6	**23.** no
11. 30, 28	

24. yes, $65 \times 12 = 780$ which is greater than 540
25. yes
26. 130
27. no, $33 \times 10 = 330$ and $330 > 250$
28. $\frac{600}{10}$ is a very rough first estimate, he overestimates because 580 is rounded up and 11.5 rounded down.

Exercise 10F (p. 160)

1. for discussion	**17.** 7000, 7401
2. 1200, 1180	**18.** 9, 9.13
3. 1000, 1079	**19.** 27, 26.55
4. 200, 217	**20.** 6, 6.13
5. 700, 668	**21.** 30 (or 39), 38.68
6. 5100 (or 4800), 5113	**22.** 6, 6.342
7. 4000, 4198	**23.** 18, 17.873
8. 7300, 7403	**24.** 2, 2.627
9. 2000, 2658	**25.** 17, 17.076
10. 9000, 8795	**26.** 5, 5.127
11. 15000, 14591	**27.** 6 (or 12), 11.81
12. 800, 854	**28.** 910
13. 600, 600	**29.** 525
14. 10000, 9917	**30.** 359
15. 5000, 5505	**31.** 193 miles
16. 2000 (or 1400), 1431	

32. a There is no delivery on Sundays **e** 912
   b 1864   **f** 3751
   c 619   **g** 3212
   d 496   **h** 13272
33. a 473 kg   **b** 495 kg
34. 9.84 kg
35. 3.68 tonnes   **51.** 5600, 5382
36. 270000, 244326   **52.** 45000, 40091
37. 12000, 11136   **53.** 54000, 51888
38. 12000, 10192   **54.** 45000, 40281
39. 36000, 34225   **55.** 24000, 22222
40. 16000, 18768   **56.** 560000, 563997
41. 7200, 7098   **57.** 24000, 23458
42. 6000, 8750   **58.** 200000, 231548
43. 30000, 32406   **59.** 480000, 465234
44. 30000, 30012   **60. a** C   **b** A
45. 7200, 6612   **61.** 8188
46. 40000, 42692   **62.** 56296 g
47. 45000, 42987   **63.** 22500
48. 50000, 46657   **64.** 1428
49. 600000, 579424   **65.** 2592
50. 300000, 298717   **66.** 672 hours

Exercise 10G (p. 164)

1. no
2. a 90   **b** 300   **c** 2000
3. 57000
4. a 16 g   **b** 24 cm   **c** 4 litres
5. a no   **b** no   **c** yes   **d** no
6. no
7. a no   **b** £8.10
8. a 1100, 1118   **d** 12, 11.57
   b 200, 257   **e** 4000, 3024
   c 21, 21.26   **f** 20000, 18392

Puzzle (p. 165)

  a ESSO   **c i** log   **ii** giggle   **iii** giles
  b Legless   **d i** 663   **ii** 36315   **iii** 0.0761

SUMMARY 2

Revision Exercise 2.1 (p. 168)

1. a $\frac{1}{3}$ **b** $\frac{1}{5}$ **c** $\frac{3}{8}$ **d** $\frac{2}{3}$ **e** $\frac{2}{5}$ **f** $\frac{2}{3}$
2. $\frac{9}{18}, \frac{6}{18}, \frac{15}{18}, \frac{10}{18}$
3. a $\frac{3}{4} = \frac{9}{12} = \frac{18}{24}$
   b $\frac{7}{10} = \frac{49}{70} = \frac{77}{110}$
   d $\frac{5}{6} = \frac{25}{30} = \frac{30}{36}$
4. a 30%   **b** 65%
5. a any one hexagon   **c** any 3 hexagons
   b any 2 hexagons
6. a $\frac{28}{100}$ **b** $\frac{30}{50}$
7. a 2.2 inches   **c** 2.8 inches
   b 6.3 cm   **d** 6.7 cm
8. a 4 tenths   **d** four
   b forty   **e** 4 tenths
   c 4 tenths
9. 4.05, 4.5, 5.04, 5.4, 5.54
10. a 0.55 cm, $\frac{55}{100}, \frac{11}{20}$ **c** 0.84 inches, $\frac{84}{100}, \frac{21}{25}$
   b 0.26 inches, $\frac{26}{100}, \frac{13}{50}$

Revision Exercise 2.2 (p. 170)

1. a 3.7   **b** 12.6   **c** 34.9   **d** 92.3
2. 4.4 m
3. a 5.76   **b** 9.08   **c** 7.16   **d** 7.45
4. a 0.57 m **b** 52 p
5. a 15.7 + 6.2 = 21.9   **c** 57.6 + 32 = 89.6
   b 2.48−.39 = 2.09   **d** 8.02 − 1.4 = 6.62
6. a 750   **b** 700
7. a 800   **b** 900   **c** 5400   **d** 45700
8. a 1300, 1292   **b** 300, 377   **c** 9000, 9207
9. no
10. a correct   **b** no   **c** no   **d** correct

Revision Exercise 2.3 (p. 171)

1. a $\frac{5}{15}$ **b** $\frac{8}{20}$ **c** $\frac{28}{48}$
2. $\frac{18}{24}, \frac{20}{24}, \frac{14}{24}, \frac{15}{24}, \frac{16}{24}, \frac{12}{24}$
3. a 59%   **b** 40%   **c** 75%
4. any three segments of each shape shaded
5. 5 and 5.0
6. a 2.87 cm   **b** 1.53 cm
7. a 5.7   **b** 1.5   **c** 8.96   **d** 27.89
8. a 0.26 seconds   **b** 20.80 seconds
9. a 6 g   **b** 14 m   **c** 4 kg
10. a 6000, 6343   **c** 11, 11.61
   b 500, 414   **d** 180000, 168489

Revision Exercise 2.4 (p. 172)

1. a 4037   **b** 293   **c** 1008
2. a 96   **b** 152
3. a Pacific   **b** Arctic   **c** 120 million square miles
4. a 4 °C   **b** 18 °C   **c** 24 °C   **d** −7 °C
5. a H, O, X **b** H, O, X, S   **c** F, J
6. a any 4 squares   **c** any 9 squares
   b any 3 squares   **d** any 3 squares
7. a 30%, 70%   **b** 40%, 60%   **c** 60%, 40%
8. a 0.76   **b** $\frac{76}{100}$ **c** $\frac{19}{25}$
9. 1.41 kg
10. a wrong   **b** correct   **c** correct   **d** wrong

Revision Exercise 2.5 (p. 175)

1. a forty   **b** 7 hundred **c** six
2. a 112   **b** 8 coaches, 21 spare seats
3. a dogs   **c** 83
   b 5   **d** dogs, cats, birds, rabbits, fish, gerbils
4. a −3 °C   **b** 5 °C   **c** −2 °C   **d** −7 °C
5. a   **b**   **c**   **d**

6. $\frac{24}{26}, \frac{24}{28}, \frac{24}{30}, \frac{24}{48}, \frac{24}{63}$
7. a As a fraction, 45 people out of 100 is $\frac{9}{20}$
   b 5 cassettes out of 20 is 25%.
8. a $\frac{4}{5}$ **b** $\frac{3}{4}$ **c** $\frac{2}{25}$ **d** $\frac{16}{25}$
9. a 5.79   **b** 14.06   **c** 4.26   **d** 2.25
10. no

Chapter 11
Coordinates

Exercise 11A (p. 177) — For discussion

Exercise 11B (p. 179)

1. **a** 5   **b** 1
2. **a** 2   **b** 6
3. **a** 9   **b** 3
4. 9
5. 7
6. 1
7. 4
8. 3
9. **a** (2, 5), (6, 2), (4, 9), (9, 1), (7, 6)
   b i 7   **ii** 3
   c i 7   **ii** 1

10.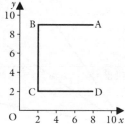
A square. Yes, 4.

14.
Letter C.

11.
Icosceles triangle. Yes, one.

15.
A tree or arrowhead.

12.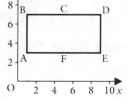
Letter M

16.
a square   **b** rectangle

13.

17. rectangle   18. (9, 3)   19. (7, 2)

20. **a i** (4, 0)   **ii** (8, 1)   **iii** (2, 7)   **iv** (15, 9)
    c rectangle
    d (8, 6), (8, 4)
22. **b** (1, 2)   **f** two of: (2, 3), (3, 4), (4, 5)
    d yes   **g** $y = x + 1$
    e i 8   **ii** 5   **h i** 3   **ii** 7   **iii** $y = x$
23. **a** 7.2 units   **b** 3.6 units   **c** DE is half AC

Exercise 11C (p. 184)

1. (5, 8)   5. (3, 6)   9. (4, 7)
2. (9, 8)   6. (8, 5)   10. (6, 3)
3. (5, 6)   7. 4 cm (or 5 units)   11. (7, 6)
4. (2, 2)   8. 3.4 cm (or 4.24 units)

12. **a** Brown Creek   **c** Bamboo Grove
    b High Pines   **d** Rocky Cove
13. **a** Bamboo Grove   **b** Black Rock
14. **a** yes   **b** no   **c** no   **d** yes

Exercise 11D (p. 187)

1. **C**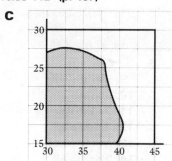

D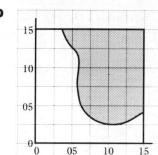

E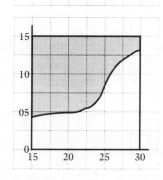

F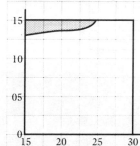

2. (05, 20)   3. (35, 15)   4. Hart

5 & 6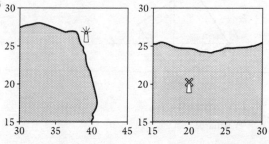

2. 31 29
3. 33 32
4. 31 27
5. 34 28
6. 30 24
7. 34 30
8. 30 25
9. Shaw Green
10. Orange End

11. Ardeley Bury
12. Mill Hill
13. Wakeley
14. Stocking Hill
15. Cromer
16. Moor Green
17. Parker's Green
18. Haymead Hill

Exercise 11F (p. 191)

1. 2, 3, 6, 1, −5, −3, 5, −3, −5, 5, 0
2. 2, −2, 5, −4, 2, 5, −5, 0
3. 5 below
4. 3 above
5. 1 below
6. 10 above
7. on the x-axis
8. 4 below

9. 3 to the right
10. 5 to the left
11. 2 to the right
12. 7 to the left
13. on the y-axis
14. 9 to the left

15. (−2, 3), (3, 1), (2, −2), (−3, 1), (1, −4), (−2, −2),
(−4, −4), (1, 2), (4, −4), (−4, 3)

16.
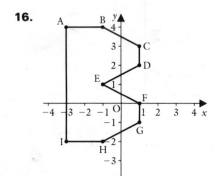

17.
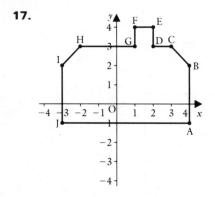

18.
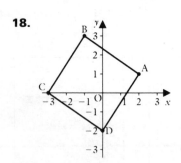

A square.

19.
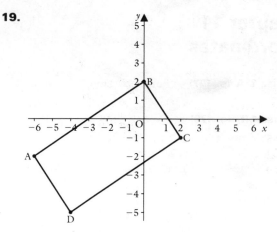

a (−4, −5)   **b** (−4, 5)

20. a
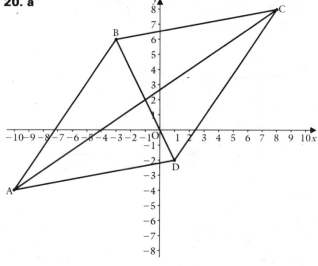

b (1, −2)   **c** (−1, 2)

21. 3 cm	28. 3.5 cm	35. (−5, 1)
22. 4 cm	29. 5.5 cm	36. (4, 2)
23. 3 cm	30. 5.5 cm	37. (2, −1)
24. 1 cm	31. (−1, 1)	38. (−4, 3)
25. 1 cm	32. (1, −2)	39. (4, 3)
26. 3.5 cm	33. (−1, 3)	40. (−1, 3)
27. 2.5 cm	34. (−6, −1)	41. (−1, 0)

Exercise 11G (p. 194)

1. A(−7, 3), B(3, 7), C(5, 2)
2. D(−5 , −2)
3. E(−2, 5)
4. outside
5. the point (3, −2)

Chapter 12
Units of Length and Mass

Exercise 12A (p. 199) — For discussion

Exercise 12B (p. 200)

2. (actual lengths)
   a 5.3 cm **b** 8.6 cm **c** 9.7 cm **d** 2.1 cm **e** 6.8 cm
3. (actual lengths)
   a 15 mm **b** 8 mm **c** 4 mm **d** 30 mm **e** 6 mm
6. 40 cm
7. **a** 900 cm
   b Yes (a large double bed is about 150 cm by 200 cm)
   c Yes (unless it was a large refectory table or work bench).

Exercise 12C (p. 202)

1. a 20 mm   **b** 600 cm   **c** 50 mm   **d** 2000 m

2. a 160 mm   **b** yes

3. a 200 mm   **b** 150 mm   **c** 90 mm   **d b** or **c**, not **a**

4. a 300 cm   **b** 2500 cm   **c** 1200 cm

5. a 2000 m   **b** 500 m, 2 km, 2500 m   **c** 5000 m

6. a 30 mm   **c** 2000 m   **e** 140 mm
    b 500 cm   **d** 2400 cm   **f** 4000 m

7. 200 cm   **12.** 150 mm   **17.** 500 cm

8. 5000 m   **13.** 6000 mm   **18.** 7000 mm

9. 30 mm   **14.** 100000 cm   **19.** 24 cm

10. 400 cm   **15.** 3000 mm   **20.** B

11. 12000 m   **16.** 2000000 mm   **21.** B

22. D (actually the record is about 41 m)

23. D

24. 3.5 m

25. $\frac{1}{2}$ m, 156 cm, 2889 mm, 3 m, 25 m

Exercise 12D (p. 205)

1. 5000 g

2. a 4000 g, 650 g, 1000 g, 1600 g
    b 4 kg
    c 650 g

3. a 3000 g   **b** 5000 g   **c** 500 g   **d** 2000 g

4. 12000 kg   **9.** 13000 g   **14.** 3000 kg

5. 3000 g   **10.** 6000 mg   **15.** 4000 mg

6. 5000 mg   **11.** 2000000 g   **16.** 700 kg of wood

7. 1000000 g   **12.** 4000 g

8. 1000000 mg   **13.** 2000000

17. shopping, 6 kg and potatoes, 5500 g

18. A   **19.** D   **20.** B   **21.** B

22. 5000 mg, 26 g, 550 g, $2\frac{1}{4}$ kg, $1\frac{1}{2}$ tonnes

Exercise 12E (p. 207)

1. 2540 g   **2.** 1300 mm   **3.** 4.3 m   **4.** 850 g

5. a 3.2 cm   **b** 500 m   **7. a** 1.46 m   **b** 5 cm

6. a 3.15 kg   **b** 1.89 kg   **8. a** 1.85 m   **b** 2.35 m   **c** yes

9. no   **18.** 5115 g   **27.** 782 cm

10. 2.8 m   **19.** 14000 g   **28.** 21 mm

11. 440 mm   **20.** 2250 g   **29.** 948 kg

12. 55.5 mm   **21.** 748 cm   **30.** 1080 mm

13. 1820 mm   **22.** 922 mm   **31.** 3500 g

14. 2456 mm   **23.** 850 g   **32.** 360 cm

15. 5059 mm   **24.** 1410 kg   **33.** 75 kg, 70.5 kg

16. 1358 mm   **25.** 19850 mg

17. 3250 g   **26.** 5420 g

34. 13.36 km, 13.64 km, assumes Newtown and Castletown in opp. direction from Old Town.

35. a 5.6 g   **b** yes

Chapter 13
Formulas

Exercise 13A (p. 211)

1. Number of drawing pins equals four times the number of posters.

2. Amount of hardcore equals the number of lorry loads multiplied by the amount of hardcore in one load.

3. Number of legs equals four times the number of four legged dining chairs.

4. Profit equals total income take away total expenditure.

5. Engine capacity equals the capacity of one cylinder times the number of cylinders.

6. The total number of tins delivered equals 48 times the number of pallets delivered.

7. a The number of wickets in use equals the number of games multiplied by 2.
    b The number of stumps is 6 times the number of games.
    c The number of bails is 4 times the number of games.
    d The number of bats is twice the number of games.

Exercise 13B (p. 213)

1. bottom number = top number + 1

2. bottom number = top number + 5

3. bottom number = top number − 3

4. bottom number = top number − 2

5. bottom number = top number × 2

6. bottom number = top number/2

7. bottom number = top number × 2

8. bottom number = top number × 3

9. bottom number = top number^2

10. bottom number = 2 × top number + 2

11. bottom number = 2 × top number − 2

12. bottom number = top number/2 − 1

13. The perimeter of a square = 4 × length of one side.

14. A distance in kilometres = 1.61 × the distance measured in miles.

15. The number of eggs in a crate = 30 × the number of trays in the crate.

16. A weight in stones = the weight in pounds/14.

17. The number of components from stock = the number of units to be assembled + 10.

18. a Profit = income − costs   **b** £0.8 m

19. a Perimeter = 2 × long side + 2 × short side
    b 38 m

20. Engine capacity = Cylinder capacity × number of cylinders, 1992 cubic centimetres.

21. a Number of cans = number of packs × 4
    b 92, 15

22. a Number of stamps = 10 × number of books
    b Cost in pence = number of books × 250 p
    c Cost in £s = number of books × £2.50
    d Number of books bought = number of £5 notes spent × 2
    e Number of stamps = number of £5 notes spent × 20

23. UK time = mainland European time − 1 hour.
Perimeter of a rectangle = 2 × length of long side + 2 × length of short side.

$$\text{Number of boxes of After Eight mints} = \frac{2 \times \text{number of guests}}{\text{number of mints in a box}}$$

24. a Tim's age = Linds'a age + 5 years
    b 7 years
    c 12 and 17 years
    d Yes, the difference in their ages stays the same.

25. a Sabina's age = Amjun's age − 3 years
    b 11 years
    c 15 years

1. The perimeter of a square is 4 times the length of one side.
2. bottom number = 2 × top number + 1
3. Number of blocks in a layer = layer number squared.
4. **a** Richard's age = Father's age − 28 years.
   b 10 years
   c 32 years

Chapter 14
Number Patterns

Exercise 14A (p. 218)

1. **a** $4+2=6, 3+3=6, 2+4=6, 1+5=6$
   b $0+6=6$
   c top left to bottom right
2. **a** $9+1=10, 8+2=10, \ldots 1+9=10$
   b as for **1c**
   c $0+10=10$
3. 27   **4.** 30   **5.** 30   **6.** 30   **7.** 26   **8.** 38

9. **a** Starting with 4, add 8 each time.
   b Starting with 9, add 18 each time.
   c Starting with 16, add 32 each time.
   d Starting with 25, add 50 each time.
10. **a** both 16   **c** as for **b**
    b always the same as each other
11. **a** both 54
    b 51, 54, 57, increasing by 3
    c 33, 54, 75, increasing by 21
    d As for **b** and **c**, also all lines of 3 passing through the centre number are equal.
12. **a** both 28
    b both 56
    c both 56
    d and **e** Outer corners, centre square and both diagonals are always the same.
13. Results will be the same, they all come from numbers in an array with 7 columns and using consecutive numbers.

Exercise 14B (p. 122)

1. $1 \times 18, 2 \times 9, 3 \times 6$
2. $1 \times 20, 2 \times 10, 4 \times 5$
3. $1 \times 24, 2 \times 12, 3 \times 8, 4 \times 6$
4. $1 \times 27, 3 \times 9$
5. $1 \times 30, 2 \times 15, 3 \times 10, 5 \times 6$
6. $1 \times 36, 2 \times 18, 3 \times 12, 4 \times 9, 6 \times 6$
7. $1 \times 40, 2 \times 20, 4 \times 10, 5 \times 8$
8. $1 \times 45, 3 \times 15, 5 \times 9$
9. $1 \times 48, 2 \times 24, 3 \times 16, 4 \times 12, 6 \times 8$
10. $1 \times 60, 2 \times 30, 3 \times 20, 4 \times 15, 5 \times 12, 6 \times 10$
11. $1 \times 64, 2 \times 32, 4 \times 16, 8 \times 8$
12. $1 \times 72, 2 \times 36, 3 \times 24, 4 \times 18, 6 \times 12, 8 \times 9$
13. $1 \times 80, 2 \times 40, 4 \times 20, 5 \times 16, 8 \times 10$
14. $1 \times 96, 2 \times 48, 3 \times 32, 4 \times 24, 6 \times 16, 8 \times 12$
15. $1 \times 144, 2 \times 72, 3 \times 48, 4 \times 36, 6 \times 24, 8 \times 18, 9 \times 16, 12 \times 12$
16. $1 \times 160, 2 \times 80, 4 \times 40, 5 \times 32, 8 \times 20, 10 \times 16$
17. $1 \times 32, 2 \times 16, 4 \times 8$
18. $1 \times 15, 3 \times 5$
19. $1 \times 42, 2 \times 21, 3 \times 14, 6 \times 7$
20. $1 \times 120, 2 \times 60, 3 \times 40, 4 \times 30, 5 \times 24, 6 \times 20, 8 \times 15, 10 \times 12$

Exercise 14C (p. 222)

1. 21, 24, 27, 30, 33, 36, 39
2. 20, 25, 30, 35, 40, 45
3. 28, 35, 42, 49, 56
4. 55, 66, 77, 88, 99
5. 26, 39, 52, 65

Exercise 14D (p. 223)

1. **a** 4, 9, 36, 49   **b** 9, 49
2. 2, 3, 5, 7, 11, 13
3. 23, 29
4. **a** 3, 19   **c** 3, 6, 9, 12, 15, 30, 36
   b 1, 9, 25, 36   **d** 1, 3, 6, 8, 12

Exercise 14E (p. 224)

1. **a** $6 \times 2 = 12, 4 \times 3 = 12, 3 \times 4 = 12, 2 \times 6 = 12, 1 \times 12 = 12$
   b because $5 \times 2.4 = 12$ so you can't make a rectangle with whole squares.
2. **a** $16 \times 4 = 64, 8 \times 8 = 64, 4 \times 16 = 64, 2 \times 32 = 64, 1 \times 64 = 64$
   b yes
   c 5 steps
3. $28 \times 2 = 56, 14 \times 4 = 56, 7 \times 8 = 56$ 3 steps
4. 1 step
5. no steps
6. Some numbers are divisible by 2 more times than others.
7. **a** 3, 6, 9, 3, 6, 9, etc
   b & **c** the digit sum of a multiple of 3 is always 3, 6, 9
8. **a** 3, 6, 2, 9, 6
   b all except 776 are divisible by 3
9. **a** 1, 4, 7, 4, 5
   b none is divisible by 3
10. true
11. all except 9247 are divisible by 3
12. (5, 1, 6, 2, 7, 3, 8, 4, 9) repeated
13. (7, 5, 3, 1, 8, 6, 4, 2, 9) repeated
14. **a** 1, 4, 9, 16, 25, 36, 49, 64, 81, 100, 121, 144, 169, 196, 225
    b (1, 4, 9, 7, 7, 9, 4, 1, 9) repeated

Exercise 14F (p. 226)

1. 1, 4, 7, 10, 13   **5.** 6, 12, 18, 24, 30
2. 5, 12, 19, 26, 33   **6.** 17, 24, 31, 38, 45
3. 1, 2, 4, 8, 16   **7.** 1, 2, 2, 4, 8
4. 1, 2, 3, 5, 8   **8.** 128, 64, 32, 16, 8

9. Start with 5, add 4 each time, 25, 29, 33
10. Start with 10, add 10 each time, 60, 70, 80
11. Start with 6, add 6 each time, 36, 42, 48
12. Start with 30, subtract 4 each time, 10, 6, 2
13. Start with 8, add 8 each time, 48, 56, 64
14. Start with 64, divide by 2 each time, 4, 2, 1
15. Start with 1, add 0.2 each time, 2.0, 2.2, 2.4
16. Start with 1, multiply by 2 and add 1, 63, 127, 255
17. 30 should be 24.   Start with 3. Multiply by 2 each time.
18. $\frac{1}{10}$ should be $\frac{1}{16}$.   Start with 1. Divide by 2 each time.
19. 14 should be 13.   Start with 2, 3. Add the two previous numbers.
20. 24 should be 25.   Start with 10. Add 1, then 2, then 3 etc.

Exercise 14G (p. 227)

1.

4	9	2
3	5	**7**
8	1	6

2. a the special number is 21

b

10	3	8
5	7	9
6	11	4

3. a the special number is 45

b

24	9	12
3	15	27
18	21	6

4.

6	9	7	12
3	16	2	13
10	5	11	8
15	4	14	1

5. a

```
        3
    2       1
        7
    6       5
        4
```

b and **c** The pairings 1 and 6, 2 and 5, 3 and 4 must all be present.

6.

```
        4
    2       3
  6     1     5
```

7.

```
        2
    6       4
  1     5     3
```

Exercise 14H (p. 229)

1. a

Triangles	1	2	3	4	5	6
Matchsticks	3	5	7	9	11	13

b 15, 17

c 2 extra

2. b the number of matchsticks will be one less than the number of sides.

3. a

Shape	Triangle.	Square	Pentagon	Hexagon
Extra matchsticks	2	3	4	5

b i 7   **ii** 9

4. d Depending on the pattern made a new square may need 1, 2 or 3 extra matchsticks.

5. a 5 by 4 rectangle of squares and a 6 by 5 rectangle.
2, 6, 12, 20, 30
Start with 2. Add 4, then add 6, etc, each time adding 2 more than you added last time.

6. 'Stairs' with 4 and 5 steps. 1, 3, 6, 10, 15
Start with 1. Add 2, then add 3 etc, each time adding 1 more than last time.

7. a

Number of tables	1	2	3	4	5	6	7	8	9	10
Number of seats **A**	6	10	14	18	22	26	30	34	38	42
Number of seats **B**	6	8	10	12	14	16	18	20	22	24

b i 7   **ii** 14

c 18 more

8. a i 13 hurdles   **ii** 22 hurdles

b The number of hurdles needed is 3 times the number of pens, plus one extra.

c 61 hurdles

d 13 pens

9. a The number of chairs is two times the number of tables, plus two.

b i 14 children   **ii** 22 children

c i 4 tables   **ii** 7 tables

10. a 8 pupils

b 3 extra

c The number of pupils seated is 3 times the number of tables, plus 2.

d 32 pupils

e 8 tables

Exercise 14I (p. 233)

1 a 40, 48   **c** 78, 158

b 37, 43

2. a $1 \times 45, 3 \times 15, 5 \times 9$ **c** 9, 16, 36 and 5, 7, 19

b 12, 18, 24, 30, 36

3. a

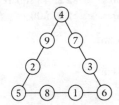

b

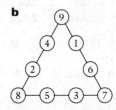

(The values given for the middle two on each edge may be reversed.)

4. a 4 and 5 triangular tables arranged in rows.

b one extra

c 12 people

d 18 tables

e The number of people seated is equal to the number of tables plus two.

5. a $2 + 7 = 9, 1 + 8 = 9, 3 + 6 = 9$ are the other possible pairings. There are several allowable combinations.

b It cannot be done. You need to add two odd numbers or two even numbers, but there are five of each. e.g. $1 + 3, 5 + 7, 2 + 4, 6 + 8$ give 4 even numbers, with 9 and 10 left over.

c This time add an odd to an even number e.g. $1 + 2, 3 + 4, 5 + 6, 7 + 8, 9 + 10$

d Yes, e.g. $1 + 2, 3 + 4, 5 + 6, 7 + 10, 8 + 9$

e i No, consider the numbers 3, 6, 9. Only two can form a pair whose sum is a multiple of 3. There is no way of pairing the third.

ii No, as for (**b**)

iii Yes, $1 + 9, 2 + 8, 3 + 7, 4 + 6, 5 + 10$

Chapter 15
Area and Perimeter

Exercise 15A (p. 236) — For discussion

Exercise 15B (p. 238)

1. $4\,cm^2$ **6.** $7\,cm^2$ **11.** $5\,cm^2$
2. $7\,cm^2$ **7.** $2\,cm^2$ **12.** $4\,cm^2$
3. $3\,cm^2$ **8.** $3.5\,cm^2$ **13.** $2.5\,cm^2$
4. $8\,cm^2$ **9.** $6\,cm^2$ **14.** $9\,cm^2$
5. $8\,cm^2$ **10.** $4\,cm^2$

15. Beech – $7\,cm^2$ Oak – $4\,cm^2$ Holly – $6\,cm^2$
Sweet chestnut – $9\,cm^2$ Sycamore – $12\,cm^2$

17. $39\,cm^2$
18. a $12\,cm^2$ **b** $1\,cm^2$
19. a 40
    b four 5 mm squares make one square with area 1 cm
    c $10\,cm^2$
    d $12\,cm^2$

Exercise 15C (p. 244)

1. a $180\,m$ **b** 6 rolls
2. a $5\,m$ **b** 4, with $\frac{2}{3}$ of a strip left over
3. $600\,cm$
4. $5\,m$
5. a square   **b** $140\,cm$
6. $5.25\,cm^2$ **8.** $6.5\,cm^2$ **10.** $2.25\,cm^2$
7. $3.5\,cm^2$ **9.** $2.5\,cm^2$ **11.** $4\,cm^2$

12. a $24\,cm$ **b** $28\,cm^2$ **15. a** $12\,cm$ **b** $5\,cm^2$
13. a $24\,cm$ **b** $24\,cm^2$ **16. a** $14\,cm$ **b** $6\,cm^2$
14. a $12\,cm$ **b** $5\,cm^2$ **17. a** $23\,cm$ **b** $12.5\,cm^2$

18. 4 squares   **20.** 6 squares   **22.** 45 squares
19. 9 squares   **21.** 6 squares   **23.** 500

24. a $18\,cm$ **b** $4.25\,cm^2$
25. 100
26. a $10.4\,cm$ **b** $5.04\,cm^2$

SUMMARY 3

Revision Exercise 3.1 (p. 250)

1.

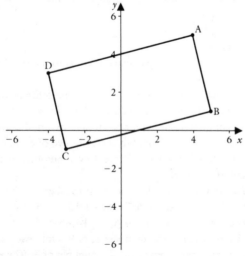

2. a E(0, 4) F(1, 0)
    b y-axis, x-axis
    c Square

3. a G(-2, -5)
    b H (6, -3)
    c i Rectangle   **ii** Square
4. a i (4, 8)   **ii** (2, 8)   **b** 2 squares
5. a Bell's Sports Centre   **d** Scott Monument
    b Perth Bridge   **e** District Council Offices
    c Railway Station
6 a $30\,mm$ **b** $500\,cm$ **c** $80\,mm$ **d** $5000\,m$
7. C
8. B
9. a $60\,mm$, by $10\,mm$ **b** $2\,km$, by $1645\,m$
10. a $64\,mm$ **c** $2720\,g$ **e** $26\,cm$
    b $600\,m$ **d** $1550\,kg$ **f** $5675\,g$

Revision Exercise 3.2 (p. 252)

1. bottom number = top number + 3
2. a The perimeter of a triangle = the sum of the lengths of
    the three sides.
    b $30\,cm$
    c $9\,cm$
3. a Norma's age = Father's age $-$ 23 years
    b 11 years
    c 42 years
4. a $1 \times 32, 2 \times 16, 4 \times 8$
    b $1 \times 108, 2 \times 54, 3 \times 36, 4 \times 27, 6 \times 18, 9 \times 12$
5. 2, 9, 16, 23, 30
6. Start with 5. Add 6 each time. 35, 41, 47
7. a $6\,cm^2$ **c** $6\,cm^2$ **e** $9\,cm^2$ **g** $9.5\,cm^2$
    b $6\,cm^2$ **d** $6\,cm^2$ **f** $10.5\,cm^2$
8. 16 squares
9. a $80\,cm^2$ **b** $62\,cm^2$ **c** $58\,cm^2$ **d** $38\,cm^2$
10. a $30\,cm$, $41\,cm^2$
    b $30\,cm$, $36\,cm^2$
    c $34\,cm$, $30\,cm^2$

Revision Exercise 3.3 (p. 254)

1. a £2   **b** £2.25
2. a wrong   **b** correct   **c** wrong   **d** correct
3. a $60\,mm$ **b** $300\,cm$ **c** $8000\,mm$ **d** $6000\,m$
4. C
5 a Number of pupils = Number of coaches $\times$ 47
    b 188 pupils
6. Bottom row = top row squared
7. a 42, 48, 54, 60, 66
    b i 5, 7, 11, 13   **ii** 9   **iii** 8, 12   **iv** 6, 12
8. a 4, 1, 7, 6, 4   **c** yes, 771
    b yes, the 4th
9. 15 squares
10. a $44\,m$ **b** $72\,cm^2$

Revision Exercise 3.4 (p. 256)

1. £3.36
2. a £160   **b** 20 stamps
3. a 56 customers
    b

Number of loaves	0	1	2	3	4	5
Frequency	12	14	21	4	3	2

    c 44
    d 90

4. A7, B8, C5, D2, E3, F4, G1, H6

5. a 79%   **b** 50%   **c** $\frac{13}{20}$

6. a 2.9 cm   **b** 33.6 cm   **c** 0.87 kg

7. a 9200   **b** 9000

8. a i 4   **ii** −2   **b i** −3   **ii** 5   **c** −3

9. bottom row = top row × 3

10. 24 squares

Revision Exercise 3.5 (p. 258)

1. a 348 + 523 = 871   **c** 927 − 564 = 363
    b 543 + 345 = 888   **d** 746 − 518 = 228

2. a 92 boxes   **b** 3 eggs

3. a Tuesday   **c** School closed
    b 830 lunches   **d** 80 more

4. a 8 − 10 = −2
    b −2 + 6 = 4, he goes from the basement to the 4th floor.
    c 11 floors
    d 15th floor

5. a $\frac{2}{3}$ **b** $\frac{3}{4}$ **c** $\frac{8}{9}$ **d** $\frac{2}{5}$ **e** $\frac{2}{7}$

6. a 1300, 1266   **c** 4, 3.969
    b 600 , 545   **d** 300000, 288304

7. a 346 mm   **d** 136 cm
    b 2214 m   **e** 775 mm
    c 217 g   **f** 4500 g

8. a Total number of seats = number of seats in one row times the number of rows.
    b 128 seats

9. 34, should be 32.   Start with 2 and double it each time.

10. a 28 cm, 49 cm²   **b** 72 cm, 288 cm²

Chapter 16
Organising and Summarising Data

Exercise 16A (p. 260) — For discussion

Exercise 16B (p. 261)

1. 6   **4.** 25 p   **7.** 10, 11   **10.** none
2. 12   **5.** 5.5 cm   **8.** red   **11.** 97, 132
3. plain   **6.** Art   **9.** 11, 12

12.

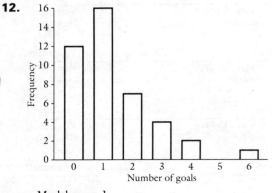

Modal score 1

13. a

Score	1	2	3	4	5	6	7	8	9	10
Frequency	1	0	2	2	3	1	5	7	5	4

b

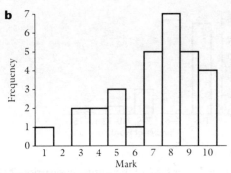

Mode   8 marks

14. 155 cm

15. 2 heads

Exercise 16C (p. 264)

1. 6   **4.** 5.5 cm   **7.** 12
2. 12   **5.** 11   **8.** 98
3. 55 p   **6.** £14.80   **9.** 1.885 cm

10. a 13 throws   **b** 3
11. a 21 pupils   **b** 4   **c** 4
12. a 2   **b** 2
13. a 30   **c** 155 cm   **e** yes
     b 156 cm   **d** Less than

14. a 132 p
    b yes, at least a half spent less than £1.32

15. You can find the most popular colour, giving the mode, but there is no way to sort the colours before finding a median.

Exercise 16D (p. 270)

1. a 47 words

b

Number of letters	1–3	4–6	7–9	10–12
Frequency	16	25	3	3

c

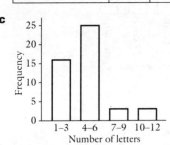

d 41 words

2. a

4	4	3	6	2	3	6	5	5	2	4	7
3	10	5	2	9	1	9	5	4	3	3	2
8	3	4	3	6	4	5	2	8	3	3	4
2	3	7	6	3	2	2	3	5	8	2	3
1	5	4	2	3	11	6	2	4	5	4	2
4	7	3	3	4	2	4	3	3	4	5	4
3	5	3	6	4	2	4	3	5	4	6	8
13	2	3	5	6	3	2	9	2	4	3	11
10	4	6	4	1	3	5	7	4	3	5	4
5	8	2	5	7	2	4	5				

b

Number of letters	1–3	4–6	7–9	10–12	13–15	Total
Frequency	48	50	13	4	1	126

c

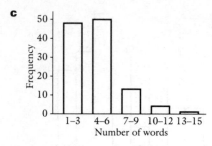

d 98 words

3. In question **1** $\frac{41}{47}$ is 0.87 of the words. In question **2** $\frac{98}{116}$ is 0.84.

The proportion of shorter words is slightly higher in question **1**.

4. a 19   **b** 11   **c** 16   **d** no

5. a 153

    b 128

    c Don't know.

    d We need to know exactly how much each child gets.

7. a 12

    b 3

    c Only know how many read '4 or 5' books.

8. a 50%

    b £42

    c No

    d

Purchase group	Percentage
Sweets	50%
Drinks	15%
Comics	30%
Stationery	5%

    e

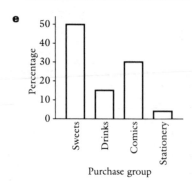

Exercise 16E (p. 274)

1. Mode 2, median 4.

2. a 59   **b** 63

    c

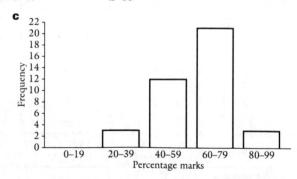

    d Less. 17 received marks of 61 and below, whereas 22 received marks greater than 61.

3. a 59   **b** 146   **c** 2   **d** 3   **e** no

Chapter 17
Probability

Exercise 17A (p. 277) — For discussion

Exercise 17B (p. 278)

1. 2 (head, tail)

2. 3 (red, blue, yellow)

3. 10 (1, 2, 3, 4, 5, 6, 7, 8, 9, 10)

4. 6 (red, yellow, blue, brown, black, green)

5. 3 (chewing gum, boiled sweets, chocolate)

6. 4 (1 p, 10 p, 20 p, 50 p)

7. 13 (Ace, 2, 3, 4, 5, 6, 7, 8, 9, 10, Jack, Queen, King)

8. 5 (A, E, I, O, U)

9. 5 (2, 3, 5, 7, 11)

10. 10 (2, 4, 6, 8, 10, 12, 14, 16, 18, 20)

11 4 (Both heads, 10 p heads & 2 p tails, 10 p tails & 2 p heads, both tails)

Exercise 17C (p. 279)

1.
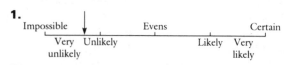

2.
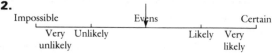

3.
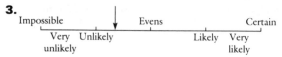

4.

5.

6.

7.
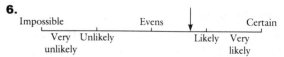

8.
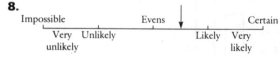

9.
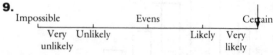

10.
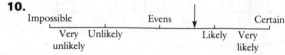

11.
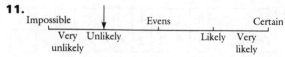

1. a 6   **b** $\frac{3}{10}$ **c** unlikely   **d** No chance

Chapter 18
Solids

Exercise 18A (p. 283) — For discussion

Exercise 18B (p. 284)

1. a & **b** In both cases the 'diagonal' lines are not what they claim to be.

2 & **3.** The front and back faces can be drawn correctly but there is no way of showing the depth accurately without labelling the diagram.

Exercise 18C (p. 285)

1, 2 & **3** All edges are drawn the length they represent.

4. c No
    d Two corners are drawn in the same place.

6. a 9 cubes
    b You can only see 8, there could be a hole at the back below **A**.

7. 10 cubes

Exercise 18D (p. 287)

2. a i 2   **ii** 2   **iii** 4 cm by 3 cm

3. 6 faces

4. b edge JI   **c** K and G

5. a edge IH   **b** B and D

6. b There are 36 arrangements altogether.
    c 11 will make a cube.

7.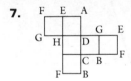

Exercise 18E (p. 291)

1. a 24 cubes   **b** 3 layers

2. a 12   **b** yes   **c** 24   **d** 24 cm^3

3. a 20   **b** 4   **c** 80   **d** 80 cm^3

4. 45 cm^3, 120 cm^3, 70 cm^3

5. a no   **b** 90 more cubes

6. exact fit

8. a 8 cm^3 **c** 16 cm^3 **e** 16 cm^3
    b 10 cm^3 **d** 16 cm^3

9. 8

10. 6

11. 8

12. 12

13. a 128   **b** 16   **c** 2

14. a 8 cm^3 **b** 48 cm^3

15. 30 cm^3

Exercise 18F (p. 295)

1. 25000 cm^3 **6.** 28000 cm^3 **11.** 62 litres

2. 5000 cm^3 **7.** 7 litres   **12.** 250 litres

3. 10000 cm^3 **8.** 2 litres   **13.** 6 litres

4. 75000 cm^3 **9.** 24 litres

5. 35000 cm^3 **10.** 51 litres

14. a 3 litres
    b 125 litres
    c 20 litres

15. 6 litres   **17.** 3 litres   **19.** no

16. 8 litres   **18.** 60 litres   **20.** 625

Exercise 18G (p. 297)

1. 16000 cm^3 **3.** 10000 cm^3

2. 64 cm^3 **4.** 30 cm^3

5.

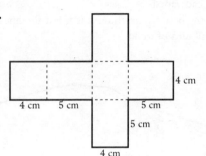

Exercise 18H (p. 297)

1. 35 litres   **3.** 512 cm^3 **5.** 47

2. 300 cm^3 **4.** the carton

Chapter 19
Line Graphs

Exercise 19A (p. 301)

1. a 36 °C   **b** 35.5 °C

2. 11 a.m.

3. 10 a.m., 2 p.m., 3 p.m.

4. No, there is no way of knowing how his temperature changed between 3 and 4 p.m.

5. Up

6. Between 1 and 2 p.m., 1.5 °C

7. Sunday

8. Wednesday

9. a £200   **b** £350

10. a £500   **b** £90

11.

Day	Sun	Mon	Tues	Wed	Thur	Fri	Sat
Takings	£0	£200	£180	£90	£320	£500	£350

12. a i November   **ii** May
    b Only between May and November.
    c No, December sales are lower than November's.
    d Autumn/Winter clothing.

Exercise 19B (p. 302)

1.–4.

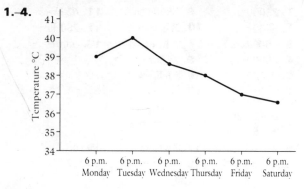

5. Tuesday and Wednesday

6. 1.5 °C

7. No, we only know evening temperatures. It could rise and fall several times in a day.

8. A curved line would imply that we knew how his temperature had varied.

9. We don't know how temperature varied, but the lines give an overall idea of trend.

10. a, b

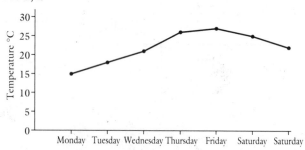

c i 27 °C   **ii** 15 °C

d i Wednesday and Thursday
ii Thursday and Friday

e Fall

f No, no information about night-time temperatures.

Exercise 19C (p. 305)

1. 25 p   **3.** 67 p   **5.** 47 p   **7.** 38 p
2. 57 p   **4.** 25 p   **6.** 25 p   **8.** 67 p

Exercise 19D (p. 305)

1.–3.

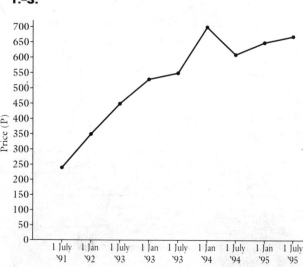

4. July '93–Jan '94

5. Jan '94–July '94

6. 700 p

7. Highly likely, we only have information for one day out of every 182/3. Anything could have happened in between.

8. Since there was an increase in the previous two periods there will probably be an increase in the next.
But, the increase in the last period was smaller than the one before, so any future increase may be small (or even non-existent).

9. a i 6 °C   **ii** 18 °C
b i 8 °C   **ii** 12 °C
c i 26 °C   **ii** 6 °C
d and **e**

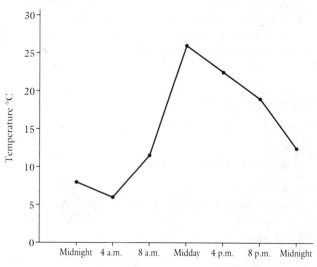

f The table is easier for parts **a** and **b**, but the graph is better for **c**.

10.

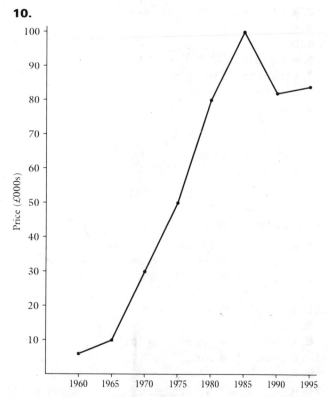

11. a £6000   **b** £84000

12. 1975–80

13. 1990–5

14. a £50000   **b** £76000

15. 1970–80 and 1975–85

Exercise 19E (p. 308)

1. 35 pints   **2.** 22.8 litres   **3.** 28 pints

4. a 19 pints   **b** too few   **c** 12 litres

5. a 44 pints   **b** Multiply by 10

6. a 28.5 litres   **b** 286 litres

7. 15 litres

8. a 2 degrees   **e** 4.5 °C

   b 1 degree   **f** 32 °F

   c i 104 °F   **ii** 38 °C   **g** 37 °C

   d 77 °F   **h** 42 °C

9. b i 28 °F   **ii** −15 °C   **d** 14 °F

   c −19 °C   **e** −31 °F

10. 50 hectares

11. 87.5 acres

12. 40 hectares

13. a 140 hectares   **c** £2500

   b 50 acres, 2.5 acres

14. 110 lb

15. 23 kg

16. 43 kg

17. 22 lb

18 a 25 kg   **b** 34 kg

Chapter 20
Time and Money

Exercise 20A (p. 313) — For discussion

Exercise 20B (p. 314)

1. no

2. five

3. a Thursday   **b** Thursday   **c** Tuesday

4. November 3rd

5. five

6. December 28th

7. a Tuesday   **b** Friday

8. August 10th

9. a Tuesday   **b** Monday

10. a Monday   **b** six   **c** five

11. 63 days

12. a 16.06.65   **b** 20.03.79   **c** 01.09.56

13. a May 31st 1998

   b 6th December or June 12th 1997

   c Put the month in words, there's no confusion then.

14. a   i 5th October 1994

    ii 3rd April 1999

    iii 15th August 2002

   b   i VII

    ii VI

    iii XV

Exercise 20C (p. 317)

1. 40 min   **3.** 9 h

2. 7 h 30 min   **4.** 1 h 15 min

5. a 9.20 a.m.   **c** 10.55 a.m.   **e** 1 h 15 min

   b 1 h 5 min   **d** 40 min

6. a 2 h 10 min   **b** 10.45 p.m.

7. 45 min

8. a 1 h 45 min   **c** 8 h 40 min

   b 2 hours   **d** 2 h 10 min

9. a 3 h 15 min   **b** 8 h 40 min   **c** 35 h 15 min

Exercise 20D (p. 320)

1. 03.20   **9.** 23.59   **17.** 10.45 a.m.

2. 11.52   **10.** 2.30 p.m.   **18.** 11.18 p.m.

3. 13.00   **11.** 9.15 a.m.   **19.** 6 h 30 min

4. 22.40   **12.** 11.20 a.m.   **20.** 8 h 29 min

5. 12.00   **13.** 8.20 p.m.   **21.** 8 hours

6. 01.00   **14.** 12.01 a.m.   **22.** 5 h 47 min

7. 21.13   **15.** 4.25 p.m.

8. 09.13   **16.** 2.06 a.m.

23. a 11.45, morning, same day

   b 15.30, afternoon, same day

   c 01.15, morning, next day

24. a 15.08 hours

   b 19.15 hours

25. 07.00 hours

26. a 2 h 22 min & 2 h 17 min

   b 20 min & 14 min

27. a Red Farm Hill & Astleton

   b Astleton & Morgan's Hollow

28. a 4 h 49 min

   b 6 h 33 min

29. a 19.45

   b 49 mins

30 a 19.27 (1 h 30 min)

   b 17.57 (1 h 46 min)

Exercise 20E (p. 323)

1. a £3.50   **b** £5.25

2. a £3   **b** £3.60   **c** £5.90

3. £2.25

4. a £36   **b** £26

5. a £1.50   **b** £4.50   **c** £1.50

6. a £1   **b** 50 p   **c** £1.50

7. £9

8. £8

9. a £1   **b** £5   **c** 50 p

10. £10.50

11. a £12   **b** £1.50

12. 50 p

13. 55 p

14. £13.25

Exercise 20F (p. 327)

1. 4 h 12 min

2. 6 h 55 min

3. 6.00 p.m.

4. a 2 h 35 min   **b** five   **c** 15.12

5. 54 days

6. £5.75

SUMMARY 4

Revision Exercise 4.1 p. 330)

1. a 1.6 g & 1.8 g   **b** 1.7 g

2. a 19 girls   **b** 10 years   **c** 11 years

3. a 17 times   **b** 3   **c** 2

4. a

Shoe size	2	3	4	5	6	7	8	9
Frequency	1	3	6	9	7	3	2	2

   b 33 pupils   **c** size 5   **d** size 5

5. a 100
 b 56
 c 69
 d No
 e

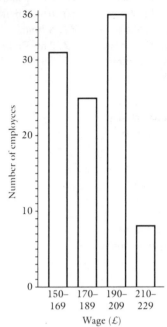

6. a 2   **b** 3   **c** 26
7. a (Ace of Spades, Ace of Hearts, Ace of Clubs,
 Ace of Diamonds)
 b (5, 10, 15, 20, 25, 30, 35)
 c (2)
8. a and **c**
9. a–d

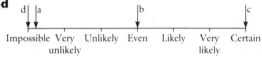

10. a Depends on when and where you do this exercise.
 b and **c**

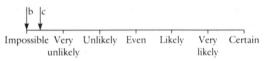

Revision Exercise 4.2 (p. 332)

1.

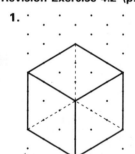

2. a 9
 b 14
 c 11 (remove 3 from the bottom layer)
 d

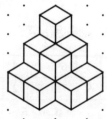

3. a 30   **b** 4   **c** 120
4. b i 6   **ii** 12
 c i 2   **ii** 2
 d 6 cm by 3 cm
 e

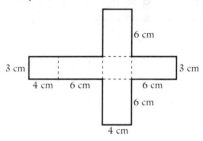

5. a i £1.50   **ii** £3   **iii** £6
 b Short term
 c Park for almost 4 hours (cost £2) then move and park
 for a further 2.5 hours (cost £1.50).
 There is no advantage in moving more often.
 Total cost £3.50, a saving of £2.50.
6.

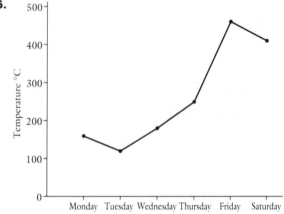

7. a Friday, £460
 b Tuesday, £120
 c i Thursday and Friday   **ii** Monday and Tuesday
 d No, no information about the spread of takings
 throughout the day.
8. a 4
 b i Thursday   **ii** Thursday   **iii** Tuesday
 c 5
 d April 9th
 e March 20th
9. a 4 h 15 min
 b 13 h 15 min
 c 15 h 10 min
10. a i £50   **ii** £170
 b £120

Revision Exercise 4.3 (p. 336)

1. a 6 and 7
 b 5, 6, 6, 6, 7, 7, 7, 9, 9   7
2. a 39   **b** 10 p   **c** 25 p
3. a (1, 2, 3, 4, 5, 6)
 b 4
4. a 18
 b 7
 c Likely (on experimental evidence)
 d 0
5. a 3000 cm^3
 b 4000 ml
 c 5 litres
 d 3500 litres

6.

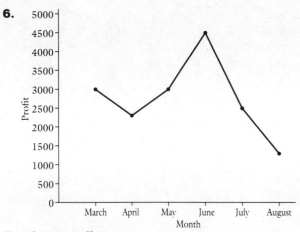

7. a i June **ii** August

b i May and June **ii** June and July

c i, ii Neither, there is no information about which week any profit is made

8. £13

9. a 30

b i 6th **ii** 18th **iii** 29th

c i Saturday **ii** Thursday **iii** Sunday

10. 20 cm by 18 cm by 7 cm

Revision Exercise 4.4 (p. 338)

1. a 118 and 119 **b** 185

2. a 2 road users **d** 8

b 34 **e** Bicycle

c 22

3. a B and F **c** A, C, D and F

b A and D

4. a 37%

b $\frac{6}{25}$

c i 12 squares

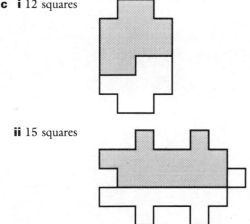

ii 15 squares

5. a i 10.1 **ii** 0.93

b 26.3 − 9.42 = 16.88

c 86 p

6. a 8000 g **c** 2000 kg **e** 6000 mm

b 5000 mg **d** 340 mm **f** 7000 ml

7. a 8 cm² **c** 8 cm² **e** 8 cm²

b 7 cm² **d** 10 cm² **f** 6 cm²

8. a i 3 to the right **ii** 2 to the right **iii** 4 to the left

b i 5 above **ii** 2 above **iii** 1 below

9. a certain **d** unlikely **g** evens

b certain **e** likely

c unlikely **f** impossible

10. a 25 g

b i 50 g **ii** 1950 g

c i Week 1 **ii** Week 6

d i No. Don't know the exact pattern of weight gain.

ii 1750 g. Half way between the weights at 3 weeks and 4 weeks old.

Revision Exercise 4.5 (p. 341)

1. a 24 × 5 = 120 **c** 34 × 8 = 272

b 18 × 4 = 72 **d** 17 × 5 = 85

2. a i £45 in credit **ii** £30 overdrawn

b i 30 + 60 = 90 **ii** 30 − 45 = −15

3. a $\frac{1}{3}, \frac{2}{3}$ **c** $\frac{2}{5}, \frac{3}{5}$

b $\frac{5}{8}, \frac{3}{8}$

4. a 4 tenths, four, 4 hundredths, forty

b i $\frac{11}{20}$ **ii** $\frac{1}{20}$ **iii** $\frac{8}{25}$ **iv** $\frac{37}{50}$

5. a 5 kg **c** 456 cm

b 36 g **d** 2 litres

6. B

7. a 3, 6, 12, 24, 48

b Start with 6. Add one, then add 2, 3, etc   27, 34, 42

8. a i 04.30 **ii** 20.15 **iii** 09.30 **iv** 16.30

b i 4.40 p.m. **iii** 12.45 p.m.

ii 6.30 a.m. **iv** 11.18 p.m.

9. a

Number of cups	Frequency
0–10	3
11–20	5
21–30	9
31–40	12
41–50	8
51–60	3
Total	40

b

```
12 |                    ___
11 |                   |   |
10 |                   |   |
 9 |              ___  |   |
 8 |             |   | |   |  ___
 7 |             |   | |   | |   |
 6 |             |   | |   | |   |
 5 |        ___  |   | |   | |   |
 4 |       |   | |   | |   | |   |
 3 |  ___  |   | |   | |   | |   |  ___
 2 | |   | |   | |   | |   | |   | |   |
 1 | |   | |   | |   | |   | |   | |   |
 0 |_0-10_11-20_21-30_31-40_41-50_51-60_
        Number of cups of tea or coffee
```

c 32 people

10. a i 8 **ii** 40

b i 50 **ii** 650 (the top layer will stick out!)

c i 3 doesn't divide 10 or 20 **ii** 38